Contents

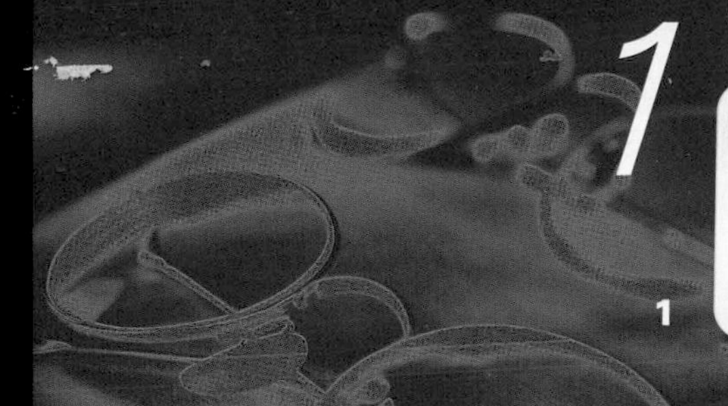

1

Who, why and how

- 1 Do you enjoy a drink?
- 2 Are you an alcoholic?
- 3 Who is this book intended for?
- 4 Who should stop drinking completely?
- 5 How do I use this book?
- 6 Check Chart

Who is this book for?

- **This book has been written for people who wish to cut down their drinking.**
- **This part of the book will help you to decide if you have a drinking problem and, if you have a problem, whether you will benefit from this book or need other advice or support.**

Do you enjoy a drink?

Why spoil a good thing? Alcohol can be enjoyable as long as you drink in a way that does you no harm.

There is absolutely no reason why you shouldn't. Alcohol gives great pleasure to millions of men and women in Scotland and many other parts of the world. Alcohol oils the wheels of social gatherings; it enables us to enjoy the company of old friends and to make new ones; it inspires song and verse; it marks important events like births, marriages and deaths, as well as the sealing of bargains and the celebration of our achievements and successes in life.

What is more, some kinds of alcoholic drink may act as a 'tonic' and some doctors recommend small amounts for a variety of minor ailments. In Britain today, a minority of adults totally abstain from alcohol. People who choose not to drink have made a decision which is sensible and appropriate for them.

However, for most of us who do drink alcohol, if it is taken in moderation and at the right time and place it can be part of a healthy lifestyle. But this book has been written for people who wish to cut down on their drinking. So why start a book which is about the dangers of alcohol by singing its praises?

The reason is that we do not want to create a false impression. Ever since you were a child, you have probably come across people who have warned against the dangers of alcohol, The people we have in mind hate any kind of drinking and try to impose their views on others. You may think that this book is just another warning against 'the demon drink'. But you would be wrong. We are not killjoys. We know that drinking can be an enjoyable thing to do. This is why we have stressed the pleasures and benefits that alcohol can bring.

But if you are **truly** to enjoy your drinking, one thing is certain. **You must drink in a way which does not do you harm. This is our object in writing this book–to help those whose drinking is doing them harm to cut down to safe levels and enjoy it once more.**

1

This book is not for alcoholics

➔ **One kind of person whose drinking is obviously doing them harm is known as an 'alcoholic'. If you think you are an alcoholic, then the book is definitely not for you.**

We had better explain what we mean by an alcoholic. It is somebody who is an 'alcohol addict'. In other words, it is somebody who drinks very large amounts of alcohol and suffers from withdrawal symptoms when he or she stops drinking. Withdrawal symptoms include 'the shakes', sweating, having fits, seeing things which aren't there, and feeling very frightened or depressed after stopping drinking.

Withdrawal symptoms are caused by the fact that your body has become accustomed to the presence of alcohol and has come to depend on alcohol to carry out its normal body functions. Therefore, when alcohol is removed, the body 'complains' about it in the form of withdrawal symptoms.

Withdrawal symptoms are very unpleasant and often the only way the sufferer can think of to get rid of them, or avoid them happening in the first place, is to have more to drink. This creates a vicious circle, with heavy drinking to avoid withdrawal symptoms, which in turn produces more withdrawal symptoms, which leads to further drinking, and so on. This vicious circle is very hard to break without medical assistance and, if you have experienced withdrawal symptoms, you are an alcohol addict and you should seek help by consulting the list of addresses at the back of this book (Part 8) or by going to your family doctor without delay.

➔ **To repeat, this book is not for alcoholics.**

1

ded for?

problems. By this we
f drinking to avoid or get
oing himself or herself harm
nd that the harm caused by

rse because you are under the
ay often miss work completely
an accident through alcohol.

be of many kinds

our family can really afford.

ause of the way you behave when
taking stupid and unnecessary

keen on your company than they
hen you were drunk. People may
amusing. Also, your whole social
bar, to the exclusion of all the other

Family

Your drinking may have caused quarrels between you and your wife or husband and your marriage may have been put at risk in this way. Or you may have been paying less attention to your children than you should. There may be other ways in which your family life is being spoiled by drinking too much.

 **Health**

You don't have to be a fully-fledged alcohol addict to damage your health by drinking too much. Did you know that whenever you have too much to drink you are risking damage to your liver? The working of your brain may also be permanently affected by regular intake of large amounts. There are many, many ways in which excessive drinking can attack your general fitness and health.

There are many, many ways in which excessive drinking can attack your general fitness and health

As well as these kinds of trouble, you may have other problems which are not actually caused by alcohol but which are made worse by drinking too much. **Try and think if this applies to you.**

You sometimes hear heavy drinkers say, 'I'm not an alcoholic. I don't have a drink problem'. There is a lot of confusion here. You may not be an alcoholic in the sense we have used the term in this book–as being physically addicted to alcohol–but if you recognise any of the types of harm just described as applying to you, then let there be no mistake about it, you have a **problem** with drinking. All this means is the presence of some problem which is related in some way to drinking alcohol. And if you have such a problem then, obviously, you should do something about it.

This book has been written to help you to do something about it. There is no magical solution to a problem with drinking and we cannot guarantee results simply from reading this book. The determination and the effort has to come from you and the book is merely intended to help you to help yourself. This is why we have called it a self-help guide.

At the same time, however, solving a problem with drinking is much more than simply a question of 'will-power'. If you use certain kinds of methods in the attempt to bring your behaviour under control, you are much more likely to succeed. This book is aimed at teaching you the best methods to use to cut down your drinking. Also, you may have tried to cut down in the past and failed. If so, this was probably because you lacked a system for cutting down. This book will show you how to reduce your drinking systematically.

Note that this is not a book which is to be read and accepted. This is a 'doing' book which sets you exercises to complete and skills to practise and which therefore requires you to participate actively.

Who should stop drinking?

You may have been under the impression that the only solution to a problem with drinking is to give up alcohol completely. This is not true and many heavy drinkers are able to reduce their drinking to amounts which are no longer harmful. However, there are certain circumstances in which you should not attempt to control your drinking but should decide to abstain altogether. These are:

1 If you have already suffered permanent medical damage from excessive drinking, then it would be very foolish to continue drinking any alcohol. If you suspect that may have harmed yourself in this way, visit a doctor immediately. You should also abstain completely if there is any medical reason why you should not drink. Again, your doctor will tell you if this is the case.

2 If you have had a drinking problem in the past and have solved it by cutting out alcohol completely, you should not be tempted by this book to return to drinking. Even if you feel that you would occasionally enjoy a drink, this cannot justify upsetting your successful adjustment to life.

3 You may simply decide that you cannot be bothered with further drinking and that you would stand a better chance of solving your problem and enjoying life more fully by cutting out alcohol completely. You must weigh up the advantages and disadvantages of stopping completely as against continuing to drink. If you prefer to cut out alcohol completely, do not let anything we have written put you off.

4 Excessive drinking by a pregnant woman harms her unborn child. It is safest if you do not drink alcohol while you are pregnant.

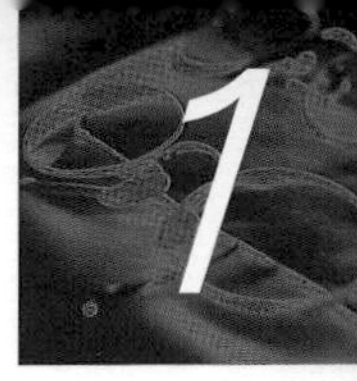

How do I use this book?

As we said before, this is a 'doing' book and there are lots of places in the book where you are asked to fill in spaces with information which applies to you.

Although this information is not especially embarrassing, we would quite understand if you felt that you didn't want anybody else to read it. In that case you should obviously keep the book in a place where others are not likely to find it. But, whether or not you wish to keep your entries private, it is absolutely essential that you fill in the tables provided in the book if you are to get any benefit from it.

Tables and quizzes

Other parts of the book provide you with facts about alcohol and drinking and we have set you a few questions to see how many of these facts you know. You are advised not to continue until you know all the correct answers in these quizzes.

Even where there are no quizzes, you should make sure you have understood everything you read before moving on. The most important thing to remember about using this book is that it's not just a book which is to be read once and then thrown aside. Rather, we advise you to use it over a period of months, or even longer. You will need to go through it slowly, making sure you have filled in all the tables and practised all the exercises. On the next page there is a 'Check Chart' which you should complete as you successfully complete each Part of the book.

After finishing the book, keep it in a handy place so that you can keep reminding yourself of what it says. Inside the back cover there is a separate pocket diary and the way to use it is explained in Part 5, page 49.

To summarise...

➔ **...this book is for you**

➔ *1* If you are not addicted to alcohol.

➔ *2* If you do have any sort of problem with drinking.

➔ *3* If you have seriously made up your mind to do something about your drinking.

➔ *4* If you are not one of those people who is better advised to stop drinking completely.

➔ *5* If you want to enjoy your drinking, in a way which does not do you harm.

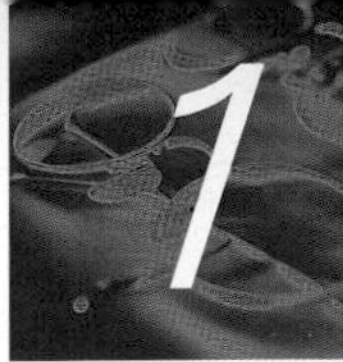

Check chart

As you complete each Part of the book use this 'Check Chart' to make sure you have not overlooked anything before moving on to the next Part.

Part 1		**yes**	**no**
1	Have you decided that his guide is suitable for you and that you will give it a real try?	X	

Part 2		**yes**	**no**
1	Do you now know how many units there are in what you drink?	X	
2	Have you begun to find out how much you drink during a typical week?	X	
3	Have you completed the chart 'During the Last Three Months'?		X
4	Have you written down your reasons for cutting down?		X
5	Have you made a 'contract' with yourself to try and cut down?	X	

Part 3		**yes**	**no**
1	Have you completed the quiz at the beginning of this Part and corrected any misunderstanding you might have had about the effects of alcohol?		
2	Do you understand the effects that alcohol has on you depend on your weight, your sex, how fast you drink, and if you've eaten beforehand?	X	
3	Do you know how the different BACs affect your behaviour and how you feel?		
4	Do you understand why tolerance to alcohol is harmful		
5	Have you completed the quiz at the end of this Part?		

Part 4		**yes**	**no**
1	Have you completed the chart?		
2	Do you understand the dangers of some reasons for drinking?	X	

Part 5		**yes**	**no**
1	Have you found someone who will help you to cut down?	X	
2	Have you started your 'Drinking Diary'?	X	
3	Do you know what circumstances are common to your troublesome drinking sessions and what circumstances are common to your troublefree sessions?		

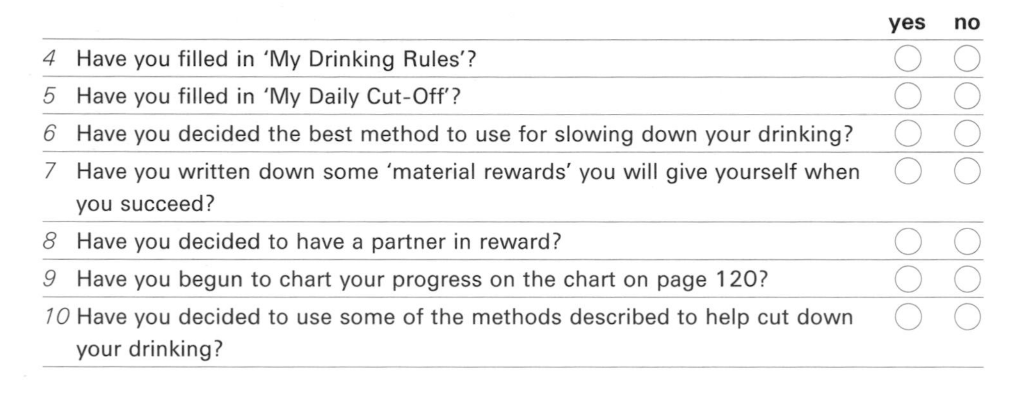

		yes	no
4	Have you filled in 'My Drinking Rules'?		
5	Have you filled in 'My Daily Cut-Off'?		
6	Have you decided the best method to use for slowing down your drinking?		
7	Have you written down some 'material rewards' you will give yourself when you succeed?		
8	Have you decided to have a partner in reward?		
9	Have you begun to chart your progress on the chart on page 120?		
10	Have you decided to use some of the methods described to help cut down your drinking?		

Part 6		yes	no
1	Do you understand how hangover symptoms are similar to anxiety symptoms?		
2	If you suffer from anxiety have you tried the methods suggested to help reduce your anxiety?		
3	Have you taken steps to start doing other things like sports, hobbies etc, as alternatives to alcohol?		
4	If the problems described in this Part are causing you to drink more, have you tried the ideas mentioned to help solve them without alcohol?		

Part 7		yes	no
1	Have you completed or started all the exercises in the previous Parts?		
2	Will you know how to cope if you have a relapse into your old drinking ways?		

Part 8		yes	no
1	When you have reached week 6 of the 'Drinking Diaries' repeat the exercise 'Four Times When Drinking Caused Me Problems'–and revise your Drinking Rules if necessary.		
2	When you have completed the diaries in the book, keep a record of your drinking for at least another twelve weeks in the 'pocket diary' at the back of the book. You should also enter your 'Methods For Cutting Down' into the pocket diary.		

2

Why should I cut down?

1 Do you really know how much you drink?

2 Other reasons for cutting down.

Why should I cut down?

- **If you've reached this far in the book, you presumably feel that you do have some sort of drinking problem and want to do something about it.**

- **The purpose of this chapter is to help you identify what kind of problem you have, so that you can tackle it more effectively.**

Do you really know how much you drink?

Before you read this Part, look over the 'Check Chart' on page 11 to make sure you have completed everything so far.

The most obvious kind of problem has to do with the amount you drink. You may simply have the feeling that you are drinking more than is good for your health. Let us see if you are right!

The first thing we have to do to decide this is to convert everything you drink into **units** of alcohol. **The basic rule is one unit equals a half-pint of beer.** A look at the table on the next page will show you the number of units there are in different drinks.

½ pint of beer or cider, 1 glass of sherry, 1 glass of table wine, 1 single whisky, vodka or gin **all equal 1 unit**

Note that the most common mistake in guessing the strength of different drinks is to underestimate the strength of beer. And one of the commonest mistakes about drinking is to think that sticking to beer can't do you any harm. Just to stress the point:

A half pint of beer equals one whisky which equals one unit
One pint of beer equals two whiskies which equals two units

How many units in your drink?

Drink	Units
1 pub measure of spirits (whisky, gin, vodka)	1
1 glass of fortified wine (sherry, martini, port)	1
1 glass of table wine	1
1 glass or can of 'alcoholic lemonade' ('alcopops')	2
1 pint of low alcohol beer	½
1 pint of beer	2
1 can of beer	1 ½
1 bottle of 'super' or 'special' lager	2 ½
1 pint of Guiness, 'real ale' or strong cider	3
1 can of 'super' or special lager	4
1 bottle of table wine	7
1 litre bottle of table wine	10
1 bottle of fortified wine (sherry, martini, port)	14
1 bottle of spirits (whisky, gin, vodka)	30

Now, we want you to think about how much you had to drink during the last typical week. First, think about what you had to drink in the seven days just past. If that week was roughly typical of your drinking, it is the week we need. If not, try and remember the most recent week which was typical–without going so far back in the past that you can't remember what happened. In the chart on page 18 we want you to try and remember what you had to drink during this typical week.

If today is Tuesday, Day 1 on the chart would be last Tuesday, Day 2 would be last Wednesday and on, until you come to Day 7 which would, of course, be yesterday. To help you, we have given an example of one day's drinking to show the sort of things you might write.

A typical week's drinking

Day	When	Where	What	Who with	Units	Total
Monday	Morning	Red Rock	1 pint	Charlie	2	
	Afternoon	Jim's Home	1 pint, 3 nips	Jim + Mary	5	13
	Evening	The Bull	3 pints	Jim	6	
	Afternoon	Red Rock	2 pints	Jim + Bob	4	

Before you start to fill in the chart, a word of warning. If heavy drinkers are asked how much they drink, they often report **less** than the true amounts. These heavy drinkers are kidding themselves. So be on your guard against completing the chart with quantities of drink which are less than you really drank on the days in question. After all, there will be only one loser if you are not completely honest about your drinking–yourself. Another point to remember is that the drinks of spirits or wine you have at home are often bigger than you would get in a pub. And a pub-measure is what we are using for our unit. So, to calculate what you have drunk at home during the last typical week, try to think how many pub-measures were poured for each glass and then add up the units.

Now fill in the chart. When you have added up the units of alcohol during each day, enter the total in the right-hand column of the chart. Then add up all seven totals to arrive at the Grand Total for the week. This is the all-important figure. We are now ready to see if you are drinking too much alcohol and need to cut down for this reason alone. But, the crucial numbers are different for men and women.

For men, the Grand Total for the week should never be more than 21 units.
For women, the Grand Total for the week should never be more than 14 units.

A typical week's drinking

Day	When	Where	What	Who with	Units	Total

Grand total for the week ______

Nearly all doctors in Scotland recommend these limits and there are two main reasons for using these particular limits. If you drink more than these amounts:

1. you increase the chance of permanently damaging your liver *and*
2. you are at risk of becoming addicted to alcohol.

Women are more likely to develop liver disease and more likely to become physically addicted to alcohol

The reason for having a lower limit for women than men is that women are more at risk for both these reasons–they are more likely to develop liver disease and more likely to become physically addicted to alcohol.

Even if your Grand Total is lower than the limit, this does not necessarily mean the your drinking is completely safe

You may be saying to yourself that these so-called safe limits are silly because nearly everyone you know, including yourself, drinks more than the limits we have given. If you are saying this, then all it means is that your friends are drinking too much as well as you! The point is that some local communities drink a lot more than others and your community may be one of them. So don't be surprised if large numbers of people you know are drinking more than is good for them. It happens only too often.

It is also essential to make clear that, even if your Grand Total is lower than the limit, this does not necessarily mean the your drinking is completely safe. And it certainly does not mean that you should increase your drinking up to the limit.

There is no level of drinking which is completely safe for everyone, just as there is no level which is dangerous for everyone.

For example, young people who have only recently started drinking may be less able to handle alcohol and weekly amounts below the limit may still be too much for them.

And another thing, your Grand Total over the week may be lower than the limit but you may still have drunk too much on one or two occasions during that week.

The safe limit does not mean that you are free to drink it all in one night!

As a final point, we must make it clear that the limits of 21 units for men and 14 units for women are certainly **not** the levels of drinking we recommend you to take. We **recommend** that you normally drink much less than this in a week and if you follow the advice we give in the book (especially in the part, 'How Can I Cut Down?'), you probably will drink less than this.

Some other reasons for cutting down...

➔ Even if your intake is fairly evenly spread and your weekly Grand Total is under the limit, you could still have a problem with your drinking. Remember that this means **any** problem related to drink. For example, keeping to the weekly 'safe' limit might be unsafe if you drive your car after drinking. You might not feel drunk, but you would still risk being arrested for drunk driving. Therefore, you **would** have a problem.

21 and 14 units are maximum upper levels you should never exceed if you want to stay healthy

On page 22 you will find a list of questions connected with drinking. If you answer 'yes' to any of these questions then, irrespective of how much you drink, you have a reason for cutting down. There is another purpose in adding to the list of problems for you to check. The problems relating to the amount you drink are not immediately obvious. For instance, in the early stages, you cannot actually see or feel anything going wrong with your liver. For this reason you may not be convinced that there is a problem to be solved. This is why we have included an extra list of problems related to drinking which have more obvious consequences. As well as the actual amount you drink, you must also pay attention to the other kinds of problems which are likely to occur.

Now read these questions on page 22 and tick the answers which apply to you. In Part 1 of this book, we told you that we were not killjoys and that we knew that drinking could be very enjoyable. That is true. But all this cannot disguise the fact that alcohol does a tremendous amount of damage in our society.

During the last three months

		yes	no
1	Have you woken up and been unable to remember some of the things you had done while drinking the previous night?	X	
2	Have you been in arguments with your family or friends because of your drinking?	X	
3	Have you found that your hands were shaking in the morning after drinking in the previous evening?	X	
4	Have you felt ashamed or guilty about your drinking?	X	
5	Has your work suffered in any way because of drinking?	X	
6	Have you found yourself neglecting any of your responsibilities because of drinking?	X	
7	Have you had a drink first thing in the morning to steady your nerves or to get rid of a hangover?	X	
8	Has there been any occasion when you felt unable to stop drinking?	X	
9	Have you feared that you were becoming dependent on alcohol?	X	
10	Have you needed a drink to face certain situations or problems?	X	
11	Have you had financial difficulties because of drink?		X
12	Have you given up hobbies, sports or other interests and spent more time drinking instead?	X	
13	Have you concealed the amount you drink from those close to you?	X	
14	Have you been drunk for several days running?	X	
15	Have you been violent after drinking?	X	
16	Have you been arrested for drunkenness?		X

If you have answered 'Yes' to any of these questions, drink is causing you problems and you do have a reason for cutting down. So carry on reading.

Do you know that, if you are a heavy drinker, then compared with light drinkers and abstainers:

1. You are **twice** as likely to die of heart disease
2. You are **twice** as likely to die of cancer
3. You are **twelve** times as likely to die of cirrhosis of the liver
4. You are **three** times as likely to die in a car crash
5. You are **six** times as likely to commit suicide.

These are just some of the harmful effects of alcohol. For all these reasons, if you suspect you may be drinking too much, but are not sure whether you can make the effort to cut down, just think what may happen to you if you do not cut down.

Now write down in the chart on page 24 the reasons for cutting down which apply to you. If you think of any good reason for cutting down which is important to you and which we have forgotten to mention then put that down too. Put each reason on a separate line and use as many lines as you need. We presume that you have definitely decided to cut down your drinking and that you have discovered the reasons for cutting down which apply to you.

It is now time to repeat something we first mentioned in Part 1. There is no magical solution to cutting down your drinking. Nobody can do it for you. All the effort and the determination has to come from you.

I shall cut down because:

Reason 1 It stops me doing things.

Reason 2 It makes me feel ill

Reason 3 It makes me tired

Reason 4 It wastes my time

Reason 5 It depresses me

Reason 6 It de-motivates me

This is why you should now pause and think carefully about the effort you will have to make. You must make up your mind not to be put off by difficulties and not to be discouraged if you do not succeed at first.

To help you summon up the determination which is needed, we are going to ask you to do something which may seem strange at first sight. But we know it works. Make a contract with yourself. Make a promise to try your best to cut down your drinking, sign it and date it. Then you will always have it to refer back to if you begin to lose heart. **Do it now**.

A contract with myself

I promise that I shall try the hardest I can to cut down my drinking so that it no longer does me harm.

Signed Margaret Gordon　　Date 5.10.06.

3

How does alcohol affect me?

How does alcohol affect me?

- **Having discovered why you should cut down your drinking, you now need to learn how alcohol affects you. But first try the quiz on page 28 to find out how much you know.**

- **If you get any answers wrong, come back to the quiz after reading this part and correct any misunderstanding you might have had about the effects of alcohol.**

Alcohol is a drug

Before you read this Part, look over the 'Check Chart' on page 11 to make sure you have completed everything so far.

Yes, that's right! We all know that heroin, cocaine, cannabis and LSD are drugs. Well, alcohol is a drug too and a powerful one at that! The most obvious difference between alcohol and the other drugs just mentioned is that alcohol is legal whereas the others are not. But misuse of alcohol causes much more damage in society than all those other drugs put together. It is worth noting what kind of drug alcohol is. It is a **depressant** drug. This means it dulls the workings of the brain and it is the same type of drug as the barbiturates which were once used as sleeping pills. Depressant drugs may make you lose some of your inhibitions and also lower your efficiency at tasks involving coordinated movements–like driving a car and many skills you perform at work. We will describe the effects of alcohol in more detail later.

You might feel 'high' when you first drink alcohol. But think of how you will feel later.

You may be surprised to learn that alcohol is a depressant drug because you have always thought of it as a stimulant. This is because it may **feel** like a stimulant at first, but this 'stimulant' effect is only shortlived, as anyone who drinks alcohol knows. By the way, mixing alcohol with other drugs can be very dangerous and is definitely not to be recommended. This includes drugs prescribed by a doctor, like sleeping pills, tranquillisers, slimming pills, anti-histamines and cough medicines. Another danger is that, when you begin to cut down your drinking, your use of other drugs may increase. For example, if you use alcohol to make you feel less anxious, you may find after you have cut down drinking that you have increased your intake of tranquillisers above the level prescribed by your doctor. So be on your guard against this.

Like other drugs, alcohol is also a deadly poison if taken in too large doses. It can cause death by knocking out the part of the brain which controls breathing. However, you have to drink a lot of alcohol in a very short space of time for this to happen and the event is fortunately rare. It usually only happens as a result of stupid drinking bets but can also occur when alcohol is consumed after taking sleeping pills.

Answers on page 92

Quiz

1	Abuse of alcohol causes as much damage in society as heroin and other hard drugs.	○ True ○ False
2	Alcohol is a stimulant drug.	○ True ○ False
3	Alcohol will warm you up on a cold day.	○ True ○ False
4	Alcohol can kill you by stopping your breathing.	○ True ○ False
5	Alcohol spreads through your body very slowly.	○ True ○ False
6	Only the liver removes alcohol from the bloodstream.	○ True ○ False
7	Alcohol contains:	○ Proteins ○ Carbohydrates ○ Vitamins.
8	How long does it take your body to get rid of the alcohol in two pints of beer?	○ Two hours ○ Three hours ○ Four hours.
9	You can sober up by:	○ Drinking lots of black coffee ○ Taking a cold shower ○ Getting some fresh air.
10	Alcohol can affect the vitamin balance of your body.	○ True ○ False
11	In two pints of beer there are:	○ 150 calories ○ 350 calories ○ 550 calories
12	Drinking spirits is more dangerous than beer.	○ True ○ False

What happens to your body when you drink alcohol?

After being swallowed, the alcohol travels to the stomach where about one-fifth of it is absorbed into the bloodstream. Unlike most other things you take in, it is not necessary for the body to digest alcohol; it can go to work straight away in the same form in which you drank it. The rest of the alcohol is absorbed through the small intestine into your blood. **Only minutes after you drink, there will be alcohol in every part of your body.**

There are certain things which slow down or speed up the rate at which alcohol is absorbed into the bloodstream and this will affect how quickly you begin to feel drunk. If you drink on an empty stomach, alcohol will travel through your body much more quickly than if you have recently had a meal. If there is food in the stomach, alcohol will be absorbed more slowly and you will not get drunk so quickly.

It is true that other ingredients in beer slow down the rate of alcohol absorption, so that intoxication is slower with beer than spirits. (But, as we have explained before, this does not mean that beer is always safe). In the opposite direction, the bubbles in champagne and other sparkling wines speed up the passage of alcohol into the bloodstream so you feel the effects more quickly. This is also true of the gas in ginger ale, tonic or soda water. It is when alcohol reaches the brain, that things start to happen. Alcohol dulls the action of the brain and, although this may feel stimulating at first, it actually has a **depressant** effect.

Alcohol will not warm you up in freezing conditions.

Often people say that alcohol warms you up. It does not. It is true that there is an immediate feeling of warmth after drinking because of a raised pulse and blood pressure. But this actually takes heat away from the body so that, if you are ever stranded in freezing conditions, drinking alcohol is not a good thing to do.

How does your body get rid of alcohol?

Less than one-tenth of the alcohol you take in is got rid of through your urine and breath. Most of it has to be burnt up by the body and this takes place in the liver. This is why the liver is one of the first parts of the body to suffer from excessive drinking. Alcohol is burnt up by the liver very slowly. In fact, it takes the liver about one hour to remove one unit of alcohol–roughly equal to a single whisky or a half pint of beer (see page 15). This slow rate at which the body gets rid of alcohol means that it remains in the system long after you have finished drinking.

Did you know that, depending on how much you have had, you can still fail a breathalyser test 12 hours after stopping drinking? This is why you should be very careful about driving the morning after you have been drinking heavily. For example, after seven pints of beer, you will probably still be over the limit eight hours later! By the way, drinking black coffee, having a cold shower or getting some fresh air, do not sober you up. At best they may help you to feel less drowsy. The only way to sober up is to do without alcohol for a period of time. In the liver, alcohol is turned into a source of energy which can be used by all the body tissues. However, although alcohol gives you energy and therefore may reduce hunger, **it does not supply the vital ingredients of your diet** e.g. carbohydrates, proteins, vitamins, etc.

Many heavy drinkers go without proper meals and, also, alcohol seems to have a direct effect on the balance of vitamins in the body. The result is that excessive drinkers are liable to suffer from several, very unpleasant diseases caused by lack of vitamins. This is on top of all the other illnesses you can get through drinking too much. And of course, alcohol makes you fat. Just drinking four pints of beer a day will add over 700 calories to your intake. Think of all the people you know who drink heavily. Many of them are overweight aren't they? So, as well as all the other damage they have done to their health, they'll have problems caused by carrying around too much weight.

Alcohol and your heart

You may have read in the newspapers that alcohol is good for your heart and prevents you from getting heart attacks. This is true to some extent but there is a lot of confusion and misunderstanding about this. **The main thing to remember is that the 'protective effect' of alcohol against heart disease applies only to moderate drinking.** And moderate means only one or two drinks a day. Regular drinking over these amounts increases the risk of illness. Another point is that moderate drinking protects against heart disease only in middle-age men and women. Younger people are unlikely to get heart attacks and their drinking has no bearing on the matter. **So please forget any impression you may have picked up in the media or in conversation that drinking large amounts is good for you. It simply isn't true.**

Your liver takes 2 hours to burn up 2 units of alcohol

In a test with taxi and bus drivers, the more they had to drink, the more certain they were that they could drive between moveable posts... and the less able they were to do it!

Alcohol and your behaviour

In the previous part (see page 16) we explained the strengths of different drinks and gave you a table for converting what you drank into units of alcohol. We must now look at the effects of these drinks on your behaviour. The effect alcohol has on you depends on the amount of alcohol in your blood. This amount is called the **Blood Alcohol Concentration** or **BAC**. Alcohol is also present in your breath, which is closely related to how much alcohol there is in your blood. BACs are usually recorded in milligrams of alcohol per 100 millilitres of blood. This can be shortened to milligrams per cent, written as mg per cent; you probably know that the legal driving limit in Britain is 80 mg per cent. The equivalent figure on the breath analyser is 35 micrograms per cent. When you drink 1 unit of alcohol (one whisky) you are likely to reach a BAC level of 15 mg (breath alcohol 6.8 micrograms per cent) and it takes your body about an hour to get rid of this. The amount of alcohol in your bloodstream doesn't just depend on how much you drink but on a number of other things.

The most important are:

1. **Your weight.** The same amount of alcohol has a greater effect on a light person than on a heavy person.
2. **Your sex.** The same amount of alcohol has a greater effect on a woman compared to a man. This is because women are on average smaller and have a lower proportion of water in their bodies to dilute the alcohol.
3. **Length of time drinking.** The same amount of alcohol if knocked back quickly will have a greater effect on you. This is because you are drinking the alcohol much faster than your liver can remove it. Therefore a greater amount of alcohol builds up in your bloodstream.
4. **Eating food.** If you have food in the stomach you will slow down the rate at which alcohol enters your blood and, therefore, reduce the effect of the alcohol to some extent.

BAC, weight and drink consumption

BAC 50 (Breath alcohol: approx. 23)

You will feel quite pleasant without being drunk. However your judgement may suffer and your chance of accidents will be increased.

	weight	1 hour	2 hours	3 hours	4 hours	5 hours
men	9 to 11 stone	2 units	3 units	4 units	4½ units	5 units
	11 to 13 stones	2½ units	4 units	5 units	5½ units	6 units
	13st. or over	3 units	4½ units	5½ units	5½ units	6 units
women	9st. or under	1½ units	2 units	2½ units	3 units	3½ units
	9 to 11 stones	2 units	2½ units	3 units	4 units	4½ units
	11st or over	2½ units	3 units	4 units	5 units	5½ units

 **BAC 80** (Breath alcohol: approx. 35)

You will lose a little self-control and your reactions may be a little slower. Although this is the legal limit for driving, it is no guarantee that you'll be fit to drive.

	weight	1 hour	2 hours	3 hours	4 hours	5 hours
men	9 to 11 stones	3½ units	4 units	5 units	5½ units	6½ units
	11 to 13 stones	4 units	5 units	6 units	6½ units	7½ units
	13 st. or over	5 units	6 units	7 units	6½ units	8 units
women	9 st. or under	2½ units	3 units	3½ units	3½ units	4 units
	9 to 11 stones	3 units	3½ units	4½ units	4½ units	5½ units
	11 st. or over	3½ units	4½ units	5½ units	5½ units	6 units

 **BAC 120** (Breath alcohol: approx. 55)

You will get merry and you may become rather clumsy and act on impulse. We suggest that this is as drunk as anyone should get even when celebrating.

	weight	1 hour	2 hours	3 hours	4 hours	5 hours
men	9 to 11 stones	5½ units	6 units	6½ units	7 units	7½ units
	11 to 13 stones	6 units	7 units	8 units	8½ units	9 units
	13 st. or over	7½ units	8½ units	9 units	9½ units	10 units
women	9 st. or under	3½ units	4 units	4½ units	4½ units	5 units
	9 to 11 stones	4½ units	5 units	5½ units	5½ units	6 units
	11 st. or over	5 units	6 units	6½ units	6½ units	7 units

How can you control the effects of alcohol?

Now that you understand more about the things which will affect the level of alcohol in your blood, you can use this to help you to control your drinking within the limits you set.

The tables on pages 32-33 describe the likely effect of a particular rate of drinking on the amount of alcohol in your blood. Tables have been produced for three different levels of alcohol in your blood (BAC). To help you understand the first table, we should consider an example. If you are a 12 stone male and you wished to know what rate of drinking would make you feel pleasant without being drunk, you should refer to the first table (BAC 50) for males. Look down the left hand column which gives the weights and read straight across from the box with 11 to 13 stones. Your answer would therefore be 2½ units in 1 hour or 4 units in 2 hours or 5 units in 3 hours or 5½ units in 4 hours. You can convert this into quantities of the actual drinks you take.

Remember that **1 unit** equals ½ pint of beer or 1 whisky or 1 glass of wine or 1 sherry

Before you study the tables for your sex and weight, you should appreciate that they only provide a rough guide as alcohol does affect different people in different ways. When choosing the BAC you want to arrive at, you will need to know what it feels like and how it affects your behaviour.

We gave you a little information on this when introducing the tables for the three BACs on pages 32-33. But here is a more complex table with the likely effects of different BACs on your feelings and behaviour. Again, because drink affects different people in different ways, this should only be used as a rough guide.

BAC	How you feel	How you behave
40	Begin to feel relaxed	Increased chance of accidents.
60	Cheerful	Poor judgement, decisions may be affected.
80	Feelings of warmth and well being	Some loss of inhibitions and self control. Slow reaction time. Driving definitely worse.
120	Talkative, excited and emotional	Uninhibited. May act on impulse.
150	Silly and confused	Speech slurred, may be aggressive.
200	Just plain drunk	Staggering, double vision, loss of memory.
300		Unconsciousness possible.
400		Unconsciousness likely.
500		Death possible.
600		Death probable.

Tolerance to alcohol

➔ We can already guess what some of you are saying about the affects of various BACs and the amounts of drink needed to reach them. You may be saying to yourself: 'These tables are daft. It would take a lot more drink than that to make me feel silly and confused', or 'It would take more than two and a half pints to make me lose any of my inhibitions'.

If you are saying something like this, if you do feel the charts and list of BAC effects greatly overestimate the effect of alcohol, then this is because you have become tolerant to alcohol. The idea of tolerance is an important one and we had better go into it in more detail.

Tolerance to a drug means that, because of your heavy use of it, it now has a lesser effect on you than it used to. Tolerance to alcohol is exactly the same kind of thing as tolerance to heroin, when a drug addict needs more and more of the drug to get his 'kick' from it. In the case of alcohol, when you first started drinking you would feel giddy and perhaps be sick after just a few pints of beer, but you may now find that you need twice as much to drink for the alcohol to have an intoxicating effect. This is why you find that the BAC list on page 35 overestimates the effect of drink. It is based on fairly inexperienced drinkers and does not take into account the tolerance which experienced drinkers have developed.

Tolerance does not mean less alcohol gets into the bloodstream or that alcohol is less damaging. In fact, because they are able to drink larger amounts, tolerant people's drinking is likely to be more damaging.

The vitally important point about tolerance is that it is the first step in addiction to alcohol and to withdrawal symptoms (see page 4). This is partly because tolerance allows you to drink in sufficiently large amounts for withdrawal symptoms to develop. We don't want to exaggerate here. Most drinkers have acquired some degree of

tolerance without it proving too harmful. But if you are highly tolerant this is definitely a danger sign. So if you find you can drink the amounts given in the chart on pages 32-33 without feeling the effects of BACs given on page 35, this probably applies to you.

Perhaps the most dangerous belief about drinking is the idea that it is a good thing to be able to 'hold your liquor' and not show the effects of it–and that this is a manly thing to do.

Apart from the waste of money involved in buying a drug which has little effect, all this ability proves is that you have drunk too much over the years and you are on the way to becoming addicted to alcohol.

We will finish this part with another quiz to check how much you now know about alcohol and its effects on you. Again, if you get answers wrong you should read the section again and return to the quiz to check that you have corrected any mistakes.

Answers on page 92

Quiz

1	Which BAC is the legal driving limit in Britain?	◯ 50 ◯ 80 ◯ 120
2	Women get drunk more easily than men.	◯ True ◯ False
3	Which of the following things will affect how quickly you get drunk	◯ Your weight ◯ When you last ate ◯ Mixing your drinks
4	At which BAC would most people pass out?	◯ 200 ◯ 300 ◯ 400
5	At which BAC is it possible to die?	◯ 300 ◯ 400 ◯ 500
6	At BAC 80 most people's driving gets worse.	◯ True ◯ False
7	A BAC of 50 will give most people at nice 'high'	◯ True ◯ False
8	BAC 120 makes most people clumsy and uninhibited.	◯ True ◯ False
9	For most people a BAC of 200 would result in staggering, double vision and loss of memory.	◯ True ◯ False
10	People who get drunk easily are far more likely to become addicted to alcohol.	◯ True ◯ False
11	It's a good thing to be able to hold your drink.	◯ True ◯ False
12	The equivalent 'breath alcohol' to BAC 80 is	◯ 25 ◯ 35 ◯ 45

4

Why do I drink?

Why do I drink?

- **There are many reasons why people drink.**
- **This part will help you work out the reasons why *you* drink.**

Reasons for drinking

Before you read this Part, look over the 'Check Chart' on page 11 to make sure you have completed everything so far.

Why do I drink?

Alcohol has almost as many uses as it has users. And it serves different purposes at different times. The drink you have on the way home from work will probably be for different reasons than the drink you take on a Saturday night. Below is a list of questions about reasons for drinking. Look over this chart very carefully and then tick 'Seldom' or 'Often' for each of the reasons. It is essential to answer as honestly as you can. We will now go over each of these reasons in turn and discuss the good and bad things about each one. When you come to each discussion, look back and remind yourself what you have answered for that particular reason.

Reason	**seldom**	**often**
1 I drink because it helps me relax.		✓
2 I drink because it is refreshing.	✓	
3 I drink because it makes me feel good.	✓	
4 I drink because of pressure from friends and workmates.	✓	
5 I drink because it is polite to do so on certain occasions.	✓	
6 I drink because I enjoy the taste.		✓
7 I drink because people I know drink.	✓	
8 I drink in order to celebrate.	✓	
9 I drink to forget my worries.		✓
10 I drink because it gives me confidence.		✓
11 I drink when I feel angry.		✓
12 I drink to be sociable.	✓	
13 I drink because there is nothing else to do.	✓	
14 I drink to pull myself together.	✓	
15 I drink because it makes me feel at ease with people.		✓

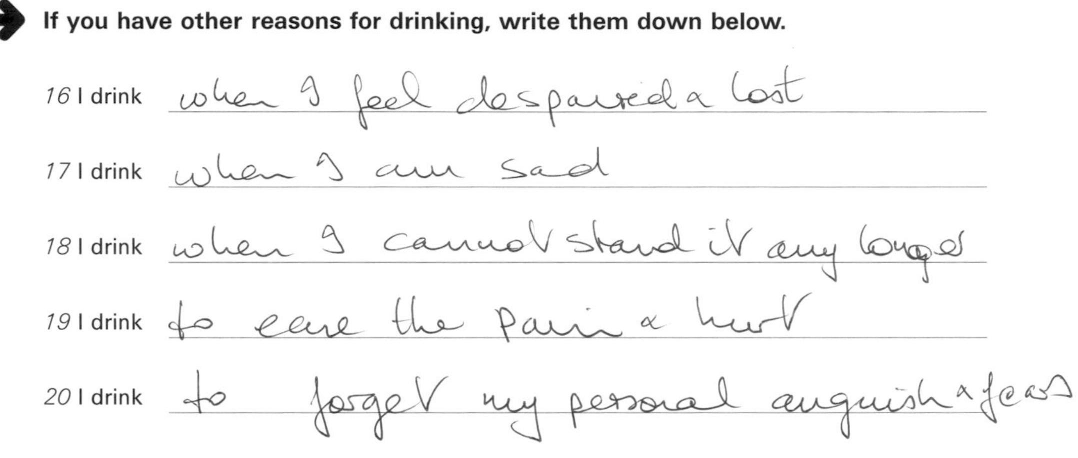

If you have other reasons for drinking, write them down below.

16 I drink when I feel desparied & lost

17 I drink when I am sad

18 I drink when I cannot stand it any longer

19 I drink to ease the pain & hurt

20 I drink to forget my personal anguish & fears

You will find that, for several of the reasons, we suggest something else you can do as an alternative to alcohol which will be explained in Part 6. So make a note of which of these alternatives is going to apply to you.

1 I drink because it helps me relax

Most people who drink have enjoyed the pleasant, relaxing effects of alcohol in the company of friends. This effect of alcohol is probably one of the main reasons why alcohol has been drunk for thousands of years in hundreds of countries. However, if you have ticked 'Often' for this reason you must ask yourself how much you need alcohol in order to relax. You must ask yourself this question because it is too easy to come to use alcohol as you use tranquillisers–and alcohol is at least as dangerous if you come to depend on it in the same way. There are other ways of learning to relax which don't involve drugs. We will discuss these in Part 6.

2 I drink because it is refreshing.

This is a good reason for drinking because it is a positive reason. If you answered 'Often' here you are not drinking because of a need, and so you are not in much danger of drinking too much when your need is not satisfied. However, as you may remember from the last chapter, alcohol is mainly a depressant drug. So how can it

be refreshing? The answer to this is that a small amount of alcohol (one or two units) seems like a stimulant in the short-term, and makes you feel more alert and hence refreshed. Once you drink more than this, the alcohol begins to have a depressant effect again.

3 **I drink because it make me feel good.**
What was said about reason one applies here also. If you begin to need alcohol in order to feel good and if it becomes difficult to feel good without alcohol, you have problems.

4 **I drink because of pressure from friends and workmates.**
Drinking is a social custom and most of us enjoy drinking with friends. But sometimes pressure from other people can lead you to drink more than you would choose to drink on your own. This is perhaps one reason why sales representatives have high rates of drinking problems–in order to do business, they often have to drink with their customers. So, as with most of these reasons, this reason for drinking is a two-edged sword. And if you have friends, relatives or workmates who are heavy drinkers, the chances are that they will try to make you a heavy drinker too. Why? Because heavy drinkers feel threatened by those who drink moderately, as they are often secretly worried and guilty about their drinking. We will discuss how to cope with pressure to drink.

5 **I drink because it is polite to do so on certain occasions.**
You **always** have the choice not to drink alcohol, if you do not want to. 'I don't want a drink tonight' should be as acceptable as 'I don't smoke'. If your drinking companions give you a hard time over this, you should ask yourself whether you should bother meeting them for a drink

6 **I drink because I enjoy the taste.**
A good reason for drinking. But heavy drinking is out because high BACs (see page 33) dull your brain's capacity to distinguish different tastes.

7 I drink because people I know drink.
What was said about reason four applies here also. Remember that you have the choice how much you drink, and you should ask yourself how often your friends or workmates want to drink heavily. Round-buying makes this especially likely because rounds made sure that everyone in the company drinks at the rate of the heaviest drinker! And if he is 15 stones and highly tolerant to alcohol (see Part 3), what he can drink without getting drunk may cause serious trouble for lighter-weight drinkers.

8 I drink in order to celebrate.
Another good reason for drinking, as long as you do not find cause for celebration several times each week!

9 I drink to forget my worries.
If you answered 'Often' for this reason, then you have a potential problem with your drinking. Now and again many drinkers get drunk in order to get rid of tension and have a 'blow out'. But if you begin to use alcohol regularly for this purpose you will probably make your worries and problems worse because alcohol is likely to make you feel more depressed and anxious in the long term.

Also, if you drink rather than face up to your worries, you are less likely to be able to do anything about them. Finally, drinking for this reason increases the risk that you will become addicted to alcohol. There are other ways of dealing with anxiety than by drinking, and we will describe them in Part 6.

10 I drink because it gives me confidence.
As was the case with reason 9, this reason for drinking has more negative sides to it than it has positive ones. Fair enough, you may drink now and again for special occasions such as making a speech at a wedding, but if you begin to need alcohol for confidence in more everyday affairs, then beware! If you feel shy, awkward or uncomfortable in company you may find some of the advice in Part 6 helpful.

➔ *11* **I drink when I feel angry.**

If you answered 'Often' to this reason for drinking, you much ask yourself why you are drinking rather than trying to change whatever it is that is making you feel angry. Perhaps you will say that you cannot change what makes you angry. But if that is the case, then drinking may well become a problem for you because you will need it a lot of the time to feel better. Often, those who have difficulty in asserting themselves–that is, saying things which may be unpleasant to the listener–become heavy drinkers. This is because alcohol can be a substitute for standing up for yourself. See Part 6 for a discussion of ways of dealing with this problem.

➔ *12* **I drink to be sociable.**

See reasons 4, 5 and 7.

➔ *13* **I drink because there is nothing else to do.**

If you ticked 'Often' for this reason, then take case. Because if drinking is the main way of occupying your free time, when you suddenly have a lot of spare time on your hands for some reason, your drinking will probably increase. This may cause problems and you may find it difficult to cut down again. See Part 6 for a discussion of other ways of dealing with boredom and a chart for your alternatives to alcohol.

➔ *14* **I drink to pull myself together.**

Another dangerous reason. Firstly, because it does not work in the long term (in fact, it has the opposite effect) and, secondly, because drinking to satisfy a need such as this may lead to a gradual increase in your drinking and possibly alcohol addiction. Why is it you need pulling together? Can you cope with stress some other way than by drinking? (See Part 6).

➔ *15* **I drink because it makes me feel at ease with other people.**

This is true for many drinkers, because alcohol is like an oil which makes the conversation flow a little more smoothly. If you begin to find it hard to enjoy company without alcohol, then it is a dangerous reason. This is especially true

Make no mistake. If you're drinking for the wrong reasons then alcohol will get a hold on you.

if you need alcohol in order to talk to someone of the opposite sex. See Part 6 for a discussion of such difficulties.

Other reasons for drinking.

You may have thought of other reasons for drinking, and there are hundreds of possible ones. For instance, some people use alcohol to help them get off to sleep. This is a tricky one, because of tolerance. If you take a certain amount of alcohol regularly, it will gradually lose its effect, and you will need more to achieve the same effect. Thus your drinking can grow out of proportion. The same thing is true if you use alcohol to relieve pain. **In general, using alcohol to relieve unpleasant feelings, or to overcome personal difficulties, is very risky**. We discuss other ways of coping with these problems in Part 5.

Drinking as a habit

Although much drinking has reasons behind it, **drinking is also a habit**. The more you drink, the more it becomes a habit and the less it has to do with the original reasons for drinking. An alcohol addict's drinking has become almost totally habitual and, as we all know, **habits are very difficult to break**. This is why some people, with no apparent personal difficulties, can become addicted to alcohol.

The drinking of almost everyone who takes alcohol is to some extent habitual but the more you drink, the more true this is.

In the next part we explain how you can set about **breaking the habit**.

5

How can I cut down?

How can I cut down?

This part of the book will give you practical advice on cutting down your drinking. But before you read it you should first look over your reasons for cutting down, listed on page 24, to remind yourself that they were good reasons.

Where to start

Before you read this Part, look over the 'Check Chart' on page 11 to make sure you have completed everything so far.

How do I cut down?

We have found it is easier for people to stick to decisions they have made if they tell others about their decisions. So why not tell your husband or wife, friends, or other people important to you that you are going to try to cut down your drinking?

Tell other people

Which of these people are you going to tell about your decision to cut down your drinking?

Who	yes	no
1 Your husband or wife?	◯	◯
2 Your boyfriend or girlfriend?	◯	◯
3 Your friends or workmates?	◯	◯
4 Your relatives or close friends?	◯	◯

Now that you are set to cut down your drinking, how should you go about it?

Your self-monitoring diary

Before you can break a habit, you must be aware of the habit. This is because habits are often unconscious–you are not aware of them. But to change them you must become conscious of them. So the first step in cutting down your drinking is to start what is called self-monitoring.

Self-monitoring simply means watching yourself and keeping a diary of when, where and exactly how much you drink. You have already done this to some extent for the last typical drinking week in Part 2. But what you should do from today is to note down every time you drink on the Drinking Diary sheets in Part 8 at the back of the book. As an example, a day in the Diary might look like the entry on the next page.

➔ The columns of the Diary are easy to understand but perhaps the column, 'Consequences of Drinking', requires some comment. Although the examples given might be regarded as bad consequences of drinking, this need not always be the case. You can put in good consequences as well. For example, 'met interesting new people' might be a good consequence of drinking. So you can put both good and bad things in 'Consequences of Drinking'. It is also clear from the example that you should make a separate entry for each drinking session. So, if you have a drink at lunchtime and go out again in the evening, you should not lump these two sessions together, but you should record each one separately in the Diary.

Over the next twelve weeks, keep a record of your drinking every day. Do not fill in the diary sheets at the end of the week. Fill them in as soon after drinking as possible, otherwise you might forget to record all of your drinks. Even after you have completed all the diary pages included in this book, you should still record in your pocket diary how many units of alcohol you drink each day. Only by keeping a close track of your drinking will you be able to see if your intake is beginning to creep up again.

➔ **So start today to record all alcoholic drinks at the back of this book.**

Drinking diary week 1

Day	Time	Hours spent	Place	Who with	Other activities	Cost	Consequences (if any)	Units
Tuesday	1-2	1	Red Rock	Tom	Eating	£5.60	Sleepy	
	5-6	1	The Bull	Jim + Tom	—	£6.40	—	10
	8-12	4	Social Club	Jim + Bob	Darts	£13	Hangover	
	1-2	1	The Bull	Tom	Eating	£5.40	—	

Risky circumstances

1 Do you find sometimes that you drink more than you meant to?

2 Do you sometimes end up regretting how much you drank the day before?

3 Does your drinking sometimes get you into trouble?

If so, we will now try to find out whether there are any particular circumstances associated with the times when you drank more than you think you should have. In other works, we will be looking for **risky circumstances** which are connected with your drinking. The way to do this is look at the last few times when drinking caused you trouble–hangovers, accidents, lateness for work, arguments in the family etc–as well as the last few times when you drank without trouble. Is there anything which distinguishes the two types of drinking occasion?

Look at the examples on page 52 which shows one person's record of drinking which caused trouble and drinking which was free of trouble. (You will see that these tables are made up in the same way as your Drinking Diary)

Troublesome drinking times

	Day	Time spent	Hours	Place	Who with	Other activities	Cost	Consequences (if any)	Units
Time 1	Fri	6-11	5	Archies Flat, The Bull	Archie, Bill + Colin	None	£15	Fell and cut hand	11
Time 2	Sat	5-10	5	Kates Bar, Chinese Rest.	Bill + Colin	Fruit Machine	£16	Arguement with Bill, went home	9
Time 3	Thur	7-11	4	Social Club	Alan, Jim + Colin	None	£14	Hangover + late for work	9
Time 4	Sat	6-12	6	Social Club	Colin, John + Alistair	None	£19	Missed bus, fell out with wife	13

Trouble-free drinking times

	Day	Time spent	Hours	Place	Who with	Other activities	Cost	Consequences (if any)	Units
Time 1	Thur	8-11	3	Social Club	Darts Team	Darts	£8		5
Time 2	Fri	8-12	4	Red Rock	Wife, Betty + Bill	Eating	£8·50		4
Time 3	Sat	9-12	3	Social Club	Bill + Archie	Dominoes	£9·25		3
Time 4	Sun	8-11	3	Kate's Bar	Alistair + John	None	£7·50		5

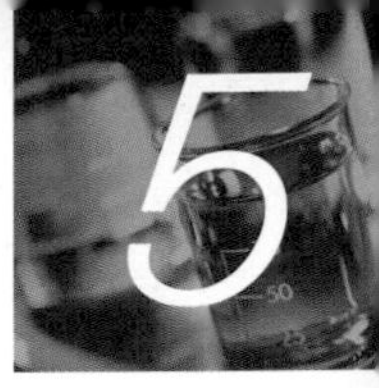

➔ Write down the circumstances common to the times when the man's drinking caused problems. Do this before reading the answers on page 54.

1 ______________________________

2 ______________________________

3 ______________________________

4 ______________________________

5 ______________________________

➔ Now write down the circumstances common to his trouble free drinking.

1 ______________________________

2 ______________________________

3 ______________________________

4 ______________________________

5 ______________________________

Typical answers

The circumstances common to the times when the man's drinking caused problems.

1 The man always began drinking at 7 o'clock or earlier when he got into trouble

2 Colin was with him each of these times

3 3 out of 4 times he drank for more than 4 hours

4 Each time he drank 9 units or more

5 3 out of 4 times he wasn't doing anything but drinking

The circumstances common to his trouble-free drinking.

1 He always began drinking at 8 o'clock or later

2 Colin was never with him on these occasions

3 He always drank for 4 or less hours

4 He never drank more than 5 units of alcohol

5 3 out of 4 times he was doing something else as well as drinking

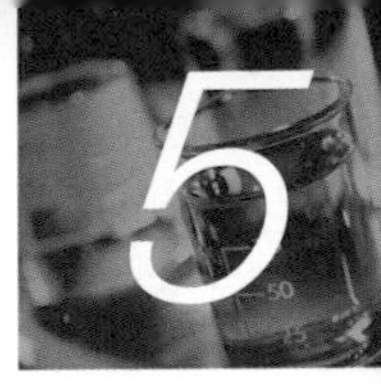

My drinking rules

1. I will never drink alcohol before 8 o'clock at night
2. I will stop drinking with Colin
3. I will never drink for over a period of 4 hours
4. I will never drink more than 5 units in one day
5. I will try to combine drinking with some other activity

The above rules are based on a number of risky circumstances which were found to apply to this man's drinking. Risky circumstances can be of several different kinds. The following are typical:

1. People you drink with–including those with whom you tend to drink too much.
2. Times when you drink–including times of day and certain days of the week, like weekend days.
3. Whether you are thirsty or hungry.
4. How you are feeling–whether you are anxious or under stress, frustrated and angry, depressed.
5. Trouble with other people–this may include rows with your wife or husband, or arguments with the boss.

There are many other kinds of risky circumstances, including those which apply to you alone and to nobody else. You may be able to think of some **personal** circumstances connected with your drinking. Now try to do this exercise for your own drinking. First, fill in the charts on page 56 and then fill in the details on the opposite page. When you have completed everything fill in 'My Drinking Rules' which you will find on page 58.

Your Drinking Rules will be based on past circumstances. However, you can also use the Drinking Diary sheets on pages 104 to 115 to do the exercises all over again in about six weeks time and change your drinking rules if necessary. We give you instructions on how to do this on page 116.

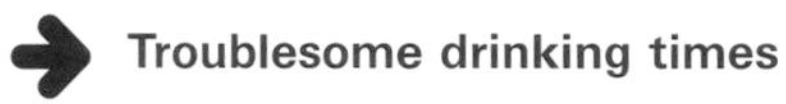

Troublesome drinking times

	Day	Time spent	Hours	Place	Who with	Other activities	Cost	Consequences (if any)	Units
Time 1									
Time 2									
Time 3									
Time 4									

Trouble-free drinking times

	Day	Time spent	Hours	Place	Who with	Other activities	Cost	Consequences (if any)	Units
Time 1									
Time 2									
Time 3									
Time 4									

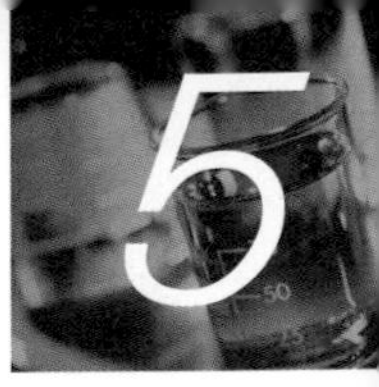

➔ What do my drinking sessions which cause trouble have in common?

1 ______________________________

2 ______________________________

3 ______________________________

4 ______________________________

5 ______________________________

➔ What do my trouble free drinking sessions have in common?

1 ______________________________

2 ______________________________

3 ______________________________

4 ______________________________

5 ______________________________

Now fill in 'My drinking rules' on the next page.

My drinking rules

1 ______________________________

2 ______________________________

3 ______________________________

4 ______________________________

5 ______________________________

An explanation

You have now made some rules about your drinking. Why do you feel the urge to drink more in some circumstances than others? The problem is that you have learned to link some situations with the urge to drink. For instance, if in the past you have often gone for a drink on the way home from work, in the future you will feel a special urge to drink on your way home from work.

If in the past you have often got drunk with certain friends, when you meet them in the future, you are more likely to feel the urge to get drunk with them. **What you must learn to do is avoid those situations where in the past you have drunk heavily or got you into trouble.** You must also **keep your drinking to those situations where in the past you have drunk moderately and without trouble.** Your Drinking Rules are aimed at helping you to do this.

One more rule

In your Drinking Rules you may have written down a rule about the maximum amount you may drink in one session. In the example given on page 52, this man had no trouble when he drank less than about 5 units of alcohol. Therefore, one of his rules was that he should never drink more than this amount (although he should try to keep well below this level). Have you a similar cut-off point? If you haven't got a cut-off point **you should have one**. Here we will explain how to decide on what your maximum daily limit should be.

First, your cut-off must be a reduction in your drinking. More than that, it must be a **meaningful reduction**–not just one or two units but a sizeable drop in intake. On the other hand, you must set yourself a realistic figure. There is no point in setting your cut-off so low that there is never any chance you are going to stick to it.

Also, although we have been examining drinking **sessions** when thinking about risky circumstances, it is much easier to set your cut-off for the whole day. Therefore the cut-off has got to be able to include the possibility of more than one drinking session in a day. For both of these reasons, try to set a **realistic** cut-off. To help you narrow down to actual figures, we insist that the cut-off you chose **must never be above 8 units per day.** And even that should be spaced over a long period of time–say five hours or more. You will normally be spending less time on drinking than this. Therefore, the conclusion is that your cut-off **must** be lower than this.

To come right down to it, we had better give you straightforward advise where you should fix your cut-off. This will depend on your sex.

For men, we recommend that your cut-off point is between 5 and 8 units.
For women, we recommend that your cut-off point is between 3 and 6 units.

Note that a cut-off doesn't mean you should drink that amount every day. Not at all! Most days you should drink less than your cut-off and we hope that on a few days per week, you will not drink at all. The cut-off is simply the amount you should never exceed in one day.

A final point is that your Daily Cut-off must take into account the maximum limit of 21 units for men and 14 units for women for your weekly Grand Total. Therefore, choose a Daily Cut-off point which permits you to keep within the weekly limit for healthy drinking.

Let us now remind you of all the points to bear in mind when choosing a Daily Cut-off for yourself.

1. The cut-off point should represent a meaningful reduction in your drinking.
2. It should also be a realistic target to aim for.
3. The cut-off point should be a daily limit which may include more than one drinking session in a day.
4. It should never be set above 8 units per day.
5. For men, we recommend a cut-off between 5 and 8 units per day.
6. For women, we recommend a cut-off between 3 and 6 units per day.
7. On most days your drinking should be well below the cut-off.
8. Your daily cut-off must be combined with a weekly limit of 21 units for men and 14 units for women.
9. If you have already made a cut-off in your drinking rules look at it again and see if it needs to be changed in the light of this discussion.

➔ **Now, taking all these factors into account, decide on your Daily Cut-off.**

➔ **My Daily Cut-off is ______ units**

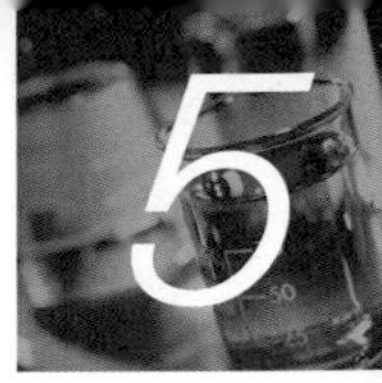

Slowing down your drinking

Even though you have set your Daily Cut-off and even though you may be beginning to drink in less risky situations, you may still be having difficulties. One common difficulty is **slowing down** your speed of drinking. If you want to drink less but still want to enjoy other people's company while drinking, **you must drink more slowly.**

This can be very difficult, because drinking is a habit and, as we have said before, **habits** are hard to break. Here are some hints about how to slow down your drinking.

1 **Pace yourself.**

a How much do you plan to drink?
b For how long do you intend to drink?
c How long must each drink last?

Answer these questions each time before you drink. For example, your answers might be:

a I plan to drink 6 units (3 pints) tonight.
b I will go out at 8.30 and come back at 11.00
c One pint must last 2½ hours divided by 3, which roughly equals 1 pint every 50 minutes.

Fifty minutes for one pint? You may think that you can't do this, but you can learn with the help of some hints below.

2 **Take smaller sips.**

As well as planning how long each drink should take, slow down the rate at which you sip your drink. **Sip less often and take smaller sips.** Count the number of sips it takes to finish your glass. Then try increasing the number on the next glass. Then try to better that and so on.

3 **Put your glass down between sips.**

Don't warm your drink in your hand. Put it down on a table or shelf after each sip. If it's in your hand, you'll drink it more often.

4 **Occupy yourself.**

Don't just drink! Do something else enjoyable while drinking that will help distract you from the glass and make you drink more slowly. Here are a few things you can do:

- *a* Reading
- *b* Chatting
- *c* Playing games such as darts, pool, draughts, dominoes, etc.
- *d* Eating (but beware of crisps and peanuts–they make you thirsty)
- *e* Listening to music.

5 **Change your drink.**

Old familiar drinks of your heavy drinking days will give you the urge to drink like that again. Be adventurous. Try stout instead of heavy or bitter. Try lager instead of stout. What about wine? If you drink spirits, change to a different one and make it a long drink with orange, tonic or other mixers. The only thing to beware of is choosing new drinks which are stronger than you think. Find out the strength of everything you try. **But remember, give up the old 'heavy-drinking' drinks.**

6 **Drink for the taste.**

Savour the taste of your drink. Let it rest on your tongue and enjoy the flavour. Don't just swill it down.

7 **Don't drink beer and spirits together.**

Why? Because you take in alcohol much faster this way.

8 **If you drink spirits, dilute them.**

The longer the drink, the slower the rate of drinking. So top them up with non-alcoholic mixers, preferably by adding more mixer than you have spirits.

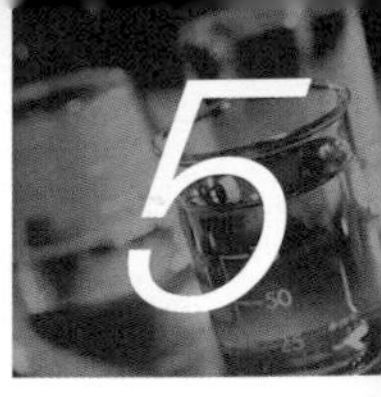

9 What about rounds?

If you regularly drink in a round-buying group, ask yourself whether you are drinking more than you would choose to if you were not in a round. There are a number of hints for dealing with this tricky problem.

Why not say to the group that you will buy your own drinks and explain why? If they reject you because of this, are they worthwhile friends anyway?

If this is difficult, buy one round (so that they know you aren't mean) then go 'solo'. Or, you can simply not buy **yourself** a drink when it is your turn to buy. That way you save money and drink less. Or you can order a 'spacer'.

10 Try a 'spacer' instead of a 'chaser'.

A 'spacer' is a non-alcoholic drink which you take in between alcoholic ones, you space them out. That way you slow down your drinking. You will be surprised how good and refreshing a spacer can be in between alcoholic ones. What about trying a non-alcoholic beer. Or, just refuse drinks every so often and accept the fact that you will pay out more than you will drink. If you get too drunk, you won't appreciate the extra drink anyway.

Finally, ask yourself whether this group in which you drink might be a 'risky situation' which is to be avoided. If that is the case, maybe the simplest way of avoiding rounds is to drop out of the group and drink with other, smaller groups of people. You might be surprised to find that someone else in the group feels the way you do. Try talking to some of them on their own and see.

11 Imitate the slow drinker.

Is there someone in the pub or in your company at home who drinks slowly? Then watch him or her–become their shadow. Don't pick up your glass until they do. Take small sips. Do something else with your hands instead of lifting the glass to your lips.

Rewarding your successes

If you think about it, most of this part so far has been concerned with making **rules**. You have written down your personal drinking rules on page 58 and you have also made a rule about the cut-off point for your drinking for any one day on page 60. We hope you have made a rule to yourself about keeping your Drinking Diary up to date every day. What is more, all the things we discussed in the last section which were aimed at helping you slow down your drinking can be thought of as setting yourself rules about the way you drink and trying to stick to them.

In this section, we are concerned with something which will make it easier for you to stick to the rules you have made. **We are concerned here with rewarding yourself every time you successfully obey one of your rules.** There are four ways in which you can reward your successes and we will take each one of them in turn.

1 **Material rewards.**

These can be almost anything you like, but there are a few things to bear in mind when choosing a material reward:

- *a* It should be something that can be given fairly soon after your success. The sooner you get the reward, the more effective it is in supporting your new behaviour
- *b* It should be something that you can easily get or afford
- *c* It should be something over and above the normal pleasures of life–something which is a luxury
- *d* It should be something which is a pleasure for you–not just something which is supposed to be a reward.

The kinds of things that can serve as rewards are: CDs, videos, audio tapes, books, magazines, games, gadgets, clothes, bits of furniture and so on; food you don't normally allow yourself; special treats like going to a good restaurant, the cinema, the theatre, to a concert etc; other things you don't often do, like making a long-distance telephone call, visiting a special friend or trying a hobby that you really enjoy.

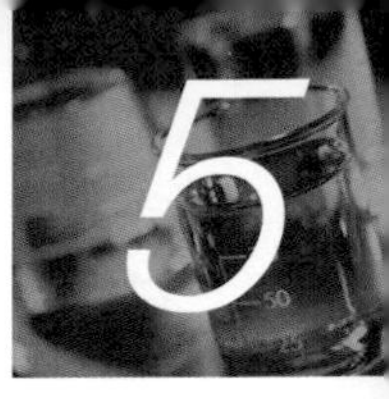

There are lots of things which can be used as rewards. But you must be sensible in choosing rewards. If you are already overweight, then more food is not a good idea. And, of course, you should never reward yourself for cutting down drinking by having another drink!

Now write down five things or activities which could serve as material rewards for you in the space below.

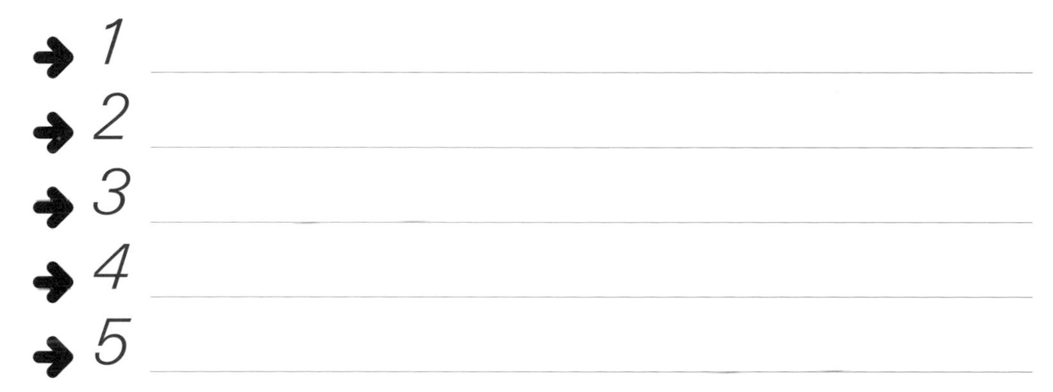

Another way of rewarding yourself is to build up small rewards gradually until they amount to something really great–something you have always wanted to own. A simple way of doing this is to work out each week how much you have saved on drink by cutting down (You can use the 'Money Spent on Alcohol' column in your Drinking Diary for this). Then put this amount away in a box, or in a special account at your bank, making a note of how much has been saved so far. When the total has reached the level you have decided on, you can spend it all on that special thing you really want. Using this method, you'll find it is very rewarding to watch your savings on drink mount up.

There are **two golden rules** to be observed in using material rewards. The first is that you must make an agreement with yourself beforehand as to what will count

as a success and what reward you will give yourself for that success. It's no use deciding on a reward **after** you have succeeded. For example, you might agree with yourself that, if you keep within your weekly Grand Total, you will reward yourself by going out to your favourite restaurant. It will help you to keep to your agreement if you write it down.

Think of all the money you could save...

The second rule is that you either succeed or fail; there are no in-betweens. For example, if you have set your Daily Cut-off at six units and you find you have had seven on a particular day, you must not say to yourself: 'I nearly made it and I deserve that reward of a new CD'. Stick rigidly to your limits and don't bend the rules. This applies to all kinds of reward we have discussed here.

2 **Mental rewards.**
This refers to talking to yourself in your head by 'singing your own praises' every time you successfully keep to a rule. This is not **crazy or childish**. We know that it is a very effective way of changing your behaviour.

The kind of things you could say to yourself might be as follows:

a 'I did really well to keep below my Daily Cut-off today'.
b 'I'm successfully keeping to my Drinking Rules and I'm getting more control over my drinking all the time.'
c 'I'm showing great determination in keeping my Drinking Diary up to date.'
d 'I succeeded very well in avoiding getting into that round. And I didn't offend anybody either.'
e 'My weekly Grand Total is below the recommended limit again and I must be getting healthier all the time.'
f 'I drank that pint more slowly than I've every managed before.'

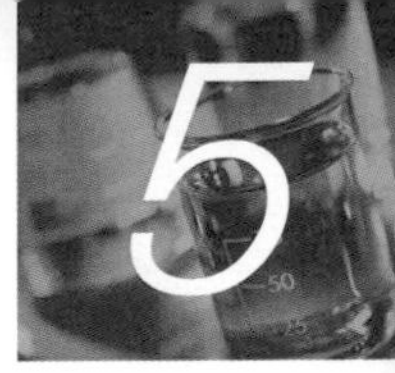

These are just a few examples and, of course, you will be able to think of many more. But these examples do make the point that mental rewards can be used for the little successes you have during the day–like drinking a drink slowly, avoiding getting into a round, politely refusing a drink you don't want, and so on. You can also use mental rewards for your larger achievements, for example keeping to your Daily Cut-off or your weekly limit. The beauty of these mental rewards is that you reward yourself immediately. And they don't cost a penny! Now write down in the space below a few things you could say to yourself for keeping to your rules. We suggest you concentrate on the obvious benefits of cutting down drinking, like looking and feeling healthier, feeling fitter, avoiding troubles from drinking, having more time to do useful things, and so on. If you fail to keep to your limits or you break other rules you have made, this is no reason to become depressed or give up trying. Instead, try to think of the lessons you can learn from the experience and how you can change things in the future.

Remind yourself of all the unpleasant results of continuing to drink too much, including those listed on page 56, and of what may happen to you if you do not succeed in controlling your drinking. These warnings to yourself can also be used if you feel the temptation to go over a limit or break some rule. Remember all the frightening things that could happen to you if you go back to your old ways and then give yourself 'a pat on the back' for having fought the temptation.

➔ 1 ______________________________

➔ 2 ______________________________

➔ 3 ______________________________

➔ 4 ______________________________

➔ 5 ______________________________

3 A partner in reward

As well as mental and material rewards, you can also use another person to give you rewards. **Choose someone close to you whom you trust** and who knows all about your efforts to cut down on your drinking.

It should not be someone who will take the opportunity to criticise or insult you. There are several ways in which your partner can be of help to you in cutting down. First of all, you can make an agreement with them that they will only reward you in some way if you keep to a rule. Remember that the reward should be something special, like cooking you a favourite meal or treating you to a night out. Also, you might agree to enjoy a certain reward together.

Apart from rewarding separate successes, your partner can also be of great help by going over your progress with you–discussing the difficulties you have come across and congratulating your successes. It could be very helpful if your trusted partner reads this book with you to understand exactly what you are trying to do. There are two ways in which you should not use a partner. Firstly, you should not ask him or her to act as a kind of policeman, by checking up on whether you have kept a rule or not. That must be entirely your own responsibility. Secondly, you should never use your partner for any kind of punishment because this can harm a good relationship.

4 Charting your progress

There is nothing so rewarding as being able to see clearly the progress you have made. For this reason we have supplied a graph for you to use on page 120. We recommend that you chart your progress on the graph because we know that this, too, is an effective way of helping you to cut down. You will be able to sit back and enjoy your successes and you will also be able to notice when you are sliding back into your bad old habits again.

So give the graph a try! Full instructions are given in Part 8, page 119.

More hints on cutting down

Here are some more things you can do to help you cut down your drinking.

Eating

Try always to eat well before drinking. You don't 'waste' the alcohol; it is absorbed more slowly and gives you a more pleasant sensation than if you drink quickly. If you eat crisps and peanuts while drinking, always have a non-alcoholic spacer with them–otherwise they will make you thirsty and you will drink more alcohol. 'Spacers' between alcoholic drinks also act like a 'food' which slows down the absorption of alcohol.

Start later

If you have not already made a rule for yourself about when to drink, think about starting drinking later than usual. Instead of going to the pub at eight, go at nine o'clock. If you usually have a drink before your evening meal, miss it out–at least sometimes.

Learn to refuse drinks.

Remember, you are the one who decides when, where and how much you drink. So rehearse ways of refusing drinks. For example, 'No thanks, I'm cutting down' or 'Not tonight, I've got a bad stomach' or 'Sorry, doctor's orders'. If people persist, ask yourself **why** are they so keen to see you drinking more. If you find refusing drinks difficult, practise by play-acting with a trusted friend or relation whom you have taken into your confidence.

Know how much you have drunk.

This is a reminder about self-monitoring. Try to record **every** drink in your Drinking Diary. If you are at a party, **measure out** your drinks. **Don't refill your glass until it is empty**–otherwise you'll lose track of what you have drunk. And **fill in your Drinking Diary every day**.

Methods for cutting down

Tick this chart, then read it every day to remind yourself of the decisions you have made.

		yes	maybe	no
1	Keeping a Drinking Diary	○	○	○
2	Keep to my personal Drinking Rules	○	○	○
3	Keep under my weekly Grand Total of 21 units (men), 14 units (women)	○	○	○
4	Pace my drinking	○	○	○
5	Sip more slowly	○	○	○
6	Take smaller sips	○	○	○
7	Occupy myself while drinking	○	○	○
8	Change my type of drink	○	○	○
9	Drink for the taste	○	○	○
10	Don't mix beer and spirits	○	○	○
11	Imitate the slow drinker	○	○	○
12	Put my glass down between sips	○	○	○
13	Tell my friends I'll buy my own drinks	○	○	○
14	Buy one round and then go 'solo'	○	○	○
15	Give myself material rewards for successes	○	○	○
16	Give myself mental rewards for successes	○	○	○
17	Chart my progress on the graphs provided	○	○	○
18	Order a spacer	○	○	○
19	Refuse drinks during some rounds	○	○	○
20	Give up drinking with round-buying groups	○	○	○
21	Dilute my spirits	○	○	○
22	Buy soft drinks in between alcoholic ones	○	○	○
23	Take at least two days rest from alcohol per week	○	○	○
24	Start drinking later	○	○	○
25	Learn to refuse drinks	○	○	○

You should have definitely ticked 'Yes' for the first four items.

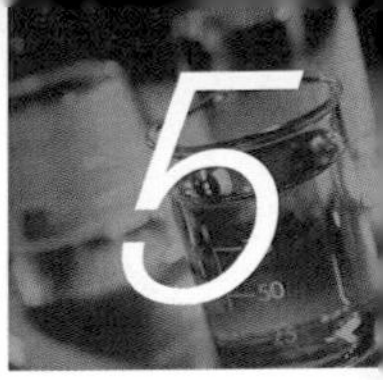

Days of rest

➜ If you drink every day, then your body and mind will miss it when you don't have a drink. If you never take a day off from alcohol, then you may well lack confidence about being able to break the habit. Abstaining a couple of days a week both boosts your confidence **and** helps you enjoy your tipple more when you take it.

Another reason for staying dry some days in the week is that you can learn to enjoy doing things without taking alcohol. Many people believe that they cannot talk easily to strangers or mix at social gatherings unless they have a drink. Because they **believe** this, they always take a drink when meeting others. But they never find out that they **can** mix without alcohol because they never try it out.

Similarly, some people never give themselves a chance to develop other interests, skills, sports or hobbies because their time is taken up with drinking.

Abstain from alcohol for at least two days per week or more

Is there something you always wanted to do?

Experiment! What about going to that car maintenance class you were always talking about? You always wanted to play a musical instrument? Go out and buy a guitar and a teach-yourself book. What about the Marathon you enjoyed watching on TV? Why not start with a little exercise or taking up a sport? Nothing makes you want to cut down more than trying to get fit. There are hundreds of opportunities which you may be missing. Give yourself a chance! So for all these reasons, as well as for reasons of health–giving your brain, liver and stomach a chance to free themselves from alcohol for a while–**abstain from alcohol for at least two days per week, and preferably more**.

Conclusions

If you use some or all of the methods we have discussed, you will stand a good chance of cutting down. However, as in changing any habit, you may well have relapses into your old ways now and again. The important thing is that, if you do have a relapse, **you must not give up**. You must say to yourself, **'I can do it'** or **'It is worth the effort'**, or something similar. Relapses are likely to occur and they do not mean that you can't cut down or that it is not worth the effort. If you jut shrug your shoulders and say, 'I learned a lot from that one', and then concentrate on getting back to your plans, you **will** have every chance of succeeding in the end.

Now let's summarise what you have learned by going over all the methods you can use for cutting down. There are some things, like keeping your Drinking Diary, trying to stick to your Drinking Rules and setting yourself a strict Daily Cut-off, which are absolutely essential to cutting down and which you must do.

You will have every chance of succeeding

The other methods are optional and whether you use some or all of them depends on the details of your particular case. But you must be patient and give each method a good try to see if it works for you. Try one at a time and gradually add each method to your way of drinking. On page 70 is a list of methods for cutting down. Look at your Drinking Rules before ticking it.

But I need to drink!

Is this true for you? If so, why? Is it because you are tense, anxious, depressed, shy, bored, lonely, lacking in confidence... **If so, then drink is not the answer.** In the next Part, we will discuss some of these problems and how you can overcome them without alcohol.

6

Be all you can be

Where to start

Reducing anxiety

Develop your self-confidence

4 Coping with problems

5 Coping with the craving for alcohol

6 Develop problem-solving skills

Be all you can be

➔ **It would be wrong to pretend that there are easy answers to all life's problems, but in this part we help you to look at some of the difficulties which may apply to you and suggest ways to make the most of your life without drinking heavily.**

Where to start

Before you read this Part, look over the 'Check Chart' on page 11 to make sure you have completed everything so far.

Drinking because you **need** to is a bad idea because it can lead to you becoming dependent on alcohol. Look back to your answers to the questionnaire on page 41 and consider to what extent you are drinking for reasons of need. There are many different needs or problems which can lead to heavy drinking, but perhaps the four most common are related to anxiety, boredom, confidence and depression.

Alcohol is a depressant drug and hence it dulls your nervous systems, making you feel less anxious. **But this is only true in the short term**. When you drink a lot, you will get hangovers–which makes you **more** anxious and you get caught in a vicious circle. Compare below some common symptoms of anxiety and common hangover symptoms. Do you see the similarities? It you drink heavily (more than 21 units a week for men or more than 14 units a week for women), then you are more likely to feel anxiety-type symptoms which are **caused** by alcohol–even though you may think that you are drinking to get rid of anxiety. Drinking to get rid of anxiety can lead to addiction.

The similarities of anxiety and hangover symptoms

Anxiety symptoms	Hangover symptoms
Shakiness	Shaking hands
Diarrhoea	Diarrhoea
Poor concentration	Poor concentration
Loss of appetite	Loss of appetite
Sweating	Sweating
Tension	-
Headache	Headache
Palpitations	Tremors
Dizziness	-
Stomach upset	Stomach upset
Breathlessness	-

Reducing Anxiety

Are you worrying about worrying?

So, how can you reduce your anxiety without abusing alcohol? This book cannot give you the complete answers, but it can point you in various directions which may be of help to you. Before we describe some ways of reducing anxiety, it must be said that anxiety can sometimes be stoked up by **fear of the symptoms of the anxiety.** People can worry about the symptoms described on this page, by sleep problems, by a pounding heart, by dizziness. **These symptoms are not dangerous**. If you can successfully detach yourself from them a little, they will go away. But if you worry about them too much, they will stay. Some people fear that they are 'cracking up' or 'going mad'. Anxiety has nothing to do with 'madness'.

Try deep, slow breathing next time you feel anxious–**relax**

Take a deep breath

You will tend to breathe quickly when you feel anxious. This can make you feel even more anxious. Shallow, quick breathing is called hyperventilation and causes anxiety-type symptoms. Try deeper, slow breathing the next time you feel anxious. The following exercise will help you:

1. Rest your fingers on the bottom of your rib cage and close your eyes.
2. Breathe in and out slowly and gently so that this part of your chest rises and falls.
3. Take one long, slow, inward breath, making sure your whole lungs are full.
4. Hold for 3 or 4 seconds.
5. Breathe out slowly, gently, and let your whole body relax as your exhale saying 'relax' to yourself as you do so.
6. Repeat this several times, and as often as you want. But do not strain yourself: do it gently.

Practise this a few times each day, try to breathe more slowly and a little more deeply.

Learn to relax

You may get tense when you are anxious. Muscle tension can cause headaches and make you feel tired. There are many ways of learning to relax. For some people, simply lying back and listening to music is enough. But there are other ways which involve learning how to control the tension in your muscles. The principle is to know when your muscles are tense and when they are relaxed. You learn to tell this by these steps:

1. Tense up one group of muscles, (say your neck muscles)
2. Notice what the feelings of tension are like
3. Relax the muscles
4. Notice the different feeling when relaxed
5. Let these feelings and the relaxation increase.

Do this for each group of muscles. You might work through them like this:

1. Right arm
2. Left arm
3. Neck
4. Scalp
5. Face
6. Shoulders
7. Back
8. Chest
9. Stomach
10. Right leg
11. Left leg.

Try practising in a quiet darkened room and leave yourself plenty of time. 15 minutes once or twice a day should be of help. If you find this difficult, do not give up.

Get up and go!

Physical exercise–swimming, running, walking, football, badminton and a hundred other sports–are a great way of relaxing. If you take regular exercise, you'll probably feel less tense and anxious. Why not try to start some form of exercise? You can't think of any? Well think back to your younger days. What sports or exercises have you done in the past? Write them down below.

Sports or exercises I have done in the past.

How about planning to take one or more of these up again? Go to your library and find out where you can do the activity you have chosen. Start slowly and gradually increase the amount of exercise you take. Yoga is a fine way of learning to relax. If you think it might suit you, go to your local library or check your local newspaper to find out where the yoga classes are in your area.

Look up your friends!

Loneliness can cause anxiety and unhappiness. If you are lonely or feel isolated, try to think of how you can meet people without necessarily drinking heavily. Are there any old friends you've drifted away from? That sometimes happens to heavy drinkers–they lose old friends because drinking becomes more important than other things. How about looking them up again?

If you are unemployed or have time on your hands, you might like to go to your Volunteer Bureau or Community Centre and ask whether you can do some voluntary work. However, if your anxiety is persistent and troublesome, your doctor may be able to refer you to someone who can help you.

Your local library may have books available about anxiety. Or check out a few bookshops to see what is available.

Let your mind run free to think of alternatives to alcohol

Coping with boredom–think about it!

Have you ever said to yourself, 'But there's nothing else to do except drink around here?' If you have, then think again, because it is not true. There is always **something** to do except drink, even though it might need some effort to arrange it.

Try some **brainstorming**. All this means is that you let your mind run free to come up with any ideas–no matter how ridiculous–about possible alternative activities to drinking. These can be anything from dominoes to tap-dancing, photography to flying.

The important thing is not to restrict your ideas. Try this exercise out with one of your family or a friend. Fill in this chart **completely** with as many possible alternatives to drinking. Don't worry just now about whether or not you have the money or opportunity to do them–just brainstorm!

Alternatives to alcohol

1 ______________________ 9 ______________________

2 ______________________ 10 ______________________

3 ______________________ 11 ______________________

4 ______________________ 12 ______________________

5 ______________________ 13 ______________________

6 ______________________ 14 ______________________

7 ______________________ 15 ______________________

8 ______________________ 16 ______________________

Think carefully about the above alternatives. Which would you enjoy most? Can you do them locally? List below those activities you intend to take up.

1 ______________________ 6 ______________________

2 ______________________ 7 ______________________

3 ______________________ 8 ______________________

4 ______________________ 9 ______________________

5 ______________________ 10 ______________________

Now make some notes on the first steps you will take to find out about these activities. (Contact local library, city information centre etc.)

alternative 1 ______________________________

alternative 2 ______________________________

alternative 3 ______________________________

alternative 4 ______________________________

alternative 5 ______________________________

alternative 6 ______________________________

6

Develop your self-confidence

➔ Some people drink because they lack confidence, feel shy or find it hard to stick up for themselves. People who find it hard to be **assertive** are more likely to drink when they feel frustrated by not sticking up for themselves.

Often such people find it hard to express anger; they will tend to bottle things up and say nothing, or say something different from what they feel. Sometimes they 'explode' much later in response to some trivial incident, when they should have been firmer at the time. Such people might have difficulty in saying 'no' to people about things in general, including when they are offered drinks. Sometimes these difficulties include shyness and low self-confidence, particularly with the opposite sex. We cannot deal with these problems properly here, though a few general comments may help.

Try out behaving as if you were confident a few times

First, 'confidence' or 'assertiveness' are skills, like driving a car or operating a machine. This means that with training and practice you learn to behave in a more confident manner. And behaving more confidently makes you **feel** more confident. You can also sometimes teach yourself these skills in the same way that you can teach yourself to operate a machine; but this is more difficult. Teach-yourself books are available in this area. But if you feel that you lack confidence, why not try out behaving as if you were confident a few times.

If someone at work asks you to do something which is not your job, stop and think. Do you normally say to yourself things like, 'I don't want to hurt his feelings by refusing' or 'It's too much trouble to refuse, I'll just do it'? If so, then what you are really saying is, 'I don't want to say "No"' or 'I am scared to say "No"'.

Well, try it and see! Try asserting yourself a few times and you'll be surprised that in most cases you'll feel much better for it and the results will be better than you feared.

Assert yourself but don't lose your cool

Your local library or bookshop will help you find titles if you want to read more about assertiveness.

But take care not to go over the top! Assert yourself, but don't lose your cool.

In some areas of the country, you can also get help in social skills training groups, or assertiveness training groups. These are provided mostly by psychologists in the National Health Service, and your family doctor may be able to refer you to one. But some Councils on Alcohol (see page 121) and other agencies are beginning to offer them also.

6

Coping with problems

Many people drink when they feel down. When you feel depressed for long periods, you can get 'stuck' in a very low emotional state. Alcohol is a depressant and guaranteed to make this worse in the long term. If you seem to have lost interest in things, if you don't seem to get pleasure out of the things you used to enjoy, then perhaps you should see your doctor about it. Depression responds well to both drug treatments and psychological treatments, if only you can drag yourself along for help.

Your local library or bookshop will help you find titles if you want to read more about depression.

However, many people feel down at times without being depressed in the sense that a doctor would use the term. But it is still dangerous to use alcohol as a drug to combat this. If you feel down, **talk to someone about it**. It's amazing how talking can help. If you can't confide in your friends or family, go to a clergyman, a doctor, a social worker or even a Citizen's Advice Bureau–because they may have details of counselling services in your area. Some Councils on Alcohol (see page 121) will offer you help even though you are not an alcoholic. Some GPs have counselling services also, so if in doubt talk to your doctor. **The important thing when you are feeling down is to find someone to talk to and don't drink alcohol.**

Bereavement

Bereavement leads to depressive feelings for quite a long time after the death of a loved-one, sometimes for more than a year. This is a particularly dangerous time to start drinking heavily because you can get hooked on alcohol, so that when you stop grieving you can't stop drinking heavily. Try to find friends and counsellors to help you through this difficult time and try to avoid using alcohol as a pain-reliever.

There is a self-help organisation called 'CRUSE' for bereaved people which may be of help. Its address is:
CRUSE (Scotland) 18 South Trinity Road Edinburgh EH5 3NR
Telephone: 0131 551 1511.

If you drink too much, there's one part that every beer can reach.

Marriage problems

Marriage problems often lead to heavy drinking in both men and women. Sometimes these problems are used as an excuse for continued heavy drinking. Sometimes cause and effect get lost in a horrible jumble of nagging, quarrelling and bad feeling. Sometimes the drinking is the cause of the problems. If you have problems with your marriage, the important thing is **talk about them**. It is sometimes astonishing how seldom two people who live together actually sit down and talk about the things which are dividing them. Shouting and accusations take the place of real communication.

Do not try to solve your problems with alcohol–if you have a problem talk to someone about it

If you find that you cannot talk coolly about your problems **find a neutral person** with whom you can talk things out. In addition to the types of people mentioned on page 121, you can go to the local marriage counselling service. A detached view of your disagreements may help you sort things out.

Sadly, however, many marriages end in divorce. Even if strife and unpleasantness has not preceded separation, actual separation or divorce can lead to feelings akin to grief in those involved. Drinking during such times can increase considerably. There are not easy answers about how to cope with these feelings, though some of the advice in this part about how to deal with depression, anxiety and isolation may be useful. A friend or someone else you can talk to may be of considerable help.

Sexual difficulties

Men who are heavy drinkers have more sexual problems than men who are not. This is largely because of the effects of alcohol which, in Shakespeare's words, 'provokes the desire, but takes away the performance'. Some men and women drink heavily because of sexual difficulties. And, of course, drinking tends to make these difficulties worse. So sexual problems are both a cause and a result of heavy drinking.

Most sexual problems can be remedied by relatively simply methods. One of the basic ways of overcoming them is to make sure that the sexual relationship is based on a warm and open emotional relationship. And the key word here is **communication**. **Talk** about your sexual worries and problems with your partner. **Discuss** what you like and don't like about your sexual relationship. This might be very difficult and embarrassing at first, but you will be surprised how easy it becomes and how much help it is.

Often, sexual impotence in a man begins when he fails to get an erection when drunk. This may make him anxious about his performance and this anxiety affects his performance even more. If, on top of all this, his partner is resentful because he has drunkenly, insensitively and selfishly had sex without showing affection, and without caring enough about her feelings, her anger may make him feel even more insecure. This can result in impotence becoming long-lasting.

However, such impotence may sometimes be quite easily remedied, though specialist help may be necessary. The key elements to overcoming these problems are showing affection, communicating and enjoying sexual preparation and foreplay without bothering too much about the end result. If you can do this, there is a good chance the problems will disappear. These pointers apply to sexual problems in women also. However, if you are in any doubt, discuss them with your GP and he or she might be able to refer you to a sex problems clinic at the local hospital. In some areas Marriage Counselling Scotland also offers sexual counselling.

Insomnia

Quite a number of people use alcohol to help them sleep. If you take a small 'night-cap' which has stayed at the same amount for the last ten years, then you need not worry too much. On the other hand, if you find that the amount you need to get you to sleep is gradually increasing, then watch out! Also, be aware that **heavy drinking often causes sleep problems.**

Be aware that heavy drinking often causes sleep problems

Try staying awake

Many of the methods for dealing with anxiety described on pages 76 to 79 may also be of use for insomnia. However, as with sexual problems, worries about performance often inhibit the performance itself. So if you lie awake at night worrying about not sleeping, do the reverse! Go to bed and try not to sleep. Wait until you are tired before going to bed, even if this is 2 or 3 o'clock in the morning. Some people only need 4 or 5 hours sleep while some need 9 or 10. Maybe you are trying to sleep more than you need to. Don't read, eat or watch TV in bed if you can't sleep. If you still have problems, see your doctor.

Unemployment

Becoming unemployed means many things for a person–most of them stressful. It can mean isolation, boredom, poverty and not knowing what to do with your time. If you are already someone who tends to drink in response to stress, and especially if you receive redundance money, then you run the risk of drinking heavily after losing your job. Again, there are no easy answers.

Structuring your day so that you are not left with too much free times is one small step towards reducing the likelihood of drinking heavily. Trying to make sure that you find some way of meeting other people regularly–for instance in a local unemployment resource centre, if there is one in your area–is another small step.

Coping with a 'craving' for alcohol

Do you sometimes feel a strong urge to drink? It may come out of the blue, or it may appear predictably in certain situations or at certain times. As craving can often feel like anxiety, you may crave alcohol when you are anxious. Boredom may also cause you to feel a strong urge to drink. Here are some alternatives when you feel the urge to drink.

Boredom may cause you to feel a strong urge to drink

Delay

Rather than drink immediately or soon after you feel the urge, delay your drinking for as long as you can. Sometimes when you do this, the urge to drink will pass. While you are delaying you can also follow the second hint.

Distraction

Craving is partly to do with your mind focusing on thoughts and images of alcohol. If you change these thoughts you will stop craving, and the best way to change them is by distracting yourself. Choose some activity that you enjoy and which is easy to do without much preparation. For instance, you could practise some relaxation methods (see page 77) or you might do some physical exercises, if circumstances allow it.

For some people, eating something might have the desired effect, while some might find that listening to music, reading, watching television or simply going for a walk would be enough to distract them from thoughts of drinking. Or perhaps you might drink a large non-alcoholic drink, for sometimes thirst can be part of craving.

If you have any hobbies or interests, immerse yourself in them for a while. If you do this, you will have a good chance of reducing the craving. But the most important thing is to have some alternative activity planned and ready so that you can recognise craving as it creeps up on you and then nip it in the bud.

Thinking

Do you find yourself saying things to yourself like, 'I really need a drink'? If these thoughts go through your mind when you are craving alcohol, then they will make the craving worse.

Challenge cravings logically–replace them with, 'I don't need a drink' or 'I don't have to drink'

These thoughts are irrational and untrue. **You don't need a drink–you may want one but you don't need it**. And why must you have a drink? The next time you feel the strong urge to drink at a time or place which conflicts with your Drinking Rules, try and pinpoint any such thoughts which are running through your mind. Then challenge them logically. Replace them with, 'I don't need a drink' or 'I don't have to drink'.

When you feel the urge to drink do something else

You can change such thoughts, but it takes a lot of practice and the most difficult part of it is to pinpoint these irrational thoughts as they occur. If you succeed in replacing them with more rational thoughts, you will be a long way towards conquering craving.

Develop problem solving skills

Many people find that they drink more heavily when they run into problems and difficulties in their lives. Problems at home, problems with money, problems at work and many others can lead people to drink heavily. Obviously some of the methods discussed above, to do with finding alternative ways of coping with anxiety, depression and lack of confidence, will be of some use in coping with life's problems. However, sometimes by taking a detached view of the problem you may more readily find a solution to it. **Problem solving skills training** is a systematic way of approaching problems in general. Here are the steps:

1 Detach yourself from the problem

This is not easy, but try to pretend that you are an outside observer. Try to stop yourself reacting to problems by saying, 'Oh no, I can't cope' or 'My life is a mess' or 'What's the point, everything's against me' because these thoughts bury you deeper in the problems and make it harder for you to see them clearly. Pretend that you are an outside consultant called in to sort out the difficulties. **Don't act impulsively**. Wait and say to yourself something like, 'I've got to stand back and look at this calmly'.

2 Spell out what the problems are

Be specific. Don't pass things off with vague phrases like, 'My marriage is no good'. Instead, say more exactly what the problems are–for example 'My wife complains that I never spend any time with her'. Or instead of saying 'I hate my job', spell out more precisely what the problem with the job is: e.g. 'I don't like my boss; he is always looking over my shoulder'.

3 Brainstorm for solutions

Remember on page 80 how you used brainstorming to come up with possible activities that you might enjoy. Well, the principle is exactly the same here, only applied to solutions to a particular problem. Examples of a few of the solutions which might emerge from brainstorming on the 'I don't like the boss…' problem are:

Nowadays there are self-help groups for many types of problem, ranging from compulsive gambling (Gamblers Anonymous) to bereavement (CRUSE).

a Leave the job.

b Ask the boss to leave you alone.

c Go out for a drink with him and talk things over.

d Ask for a transfer to another boss.

e Shout at him the next time he seems to be pestering you.

f Complain to his superior.

g Ask him why he feels he has to watch you.

h Get together with the other employees and form a deputation.

i Ignore him and don't let it get to you.

4 Decide on the best solution

Having seen the problems in a fairly detached way and having come up with some possible solutions, now is the time to weed out the impractical solutions. Go over the most likely ones with a friend, minister, priest or some other fairly neutral person. Then decide on your course of action.

5 Try out the solution

Ask at your Citizens' Advice Bureau whether there is an organisation catering for your needs in your area.

But be ready to change the decision if, after a fair try, it appears not to be the right one. Where the solution required you to do something which doesn't come easy to you, try to practise it in advance. For instance, if you have decided that you have to confront the boss, practise how you are going to set about it–either on your own or preferably with a friend or relative. These very crude guidelines may be of some help to you in sorting out your problems, though not all problems have solutions. Where possible, try to work out your difficulties with some neutral person. This makes it easier to achieve the detachment necessary to solve problems. Don't bottle up your worries. Also check in some large bookshops, where 'self-help books' are available on many types of problem. But, whatever your problem, never forget this simple fact: **Heavy drinking makes your problems worse!**

Answers to the quiz on page 28

1 False. It causes many times more damage.
2 False. It is a depressant drug.
3 False. It takes heat away from the body.
4 True. But only after drinking very large amounts very rapidly.
5 False. It takes only a few minutes.
6 True for all practical purposes. That's why the liver gets overworked if you drink too much.
7 No. No. No.
8 Four hours.
9 All false. Only time can sober you up.
10 True. It gives you nutritional problems.
11 550.
12 False. Remember, a half-pint of beer is just as strong as one measure of spirits.

Answers to the quiz on page 38

1 BAC 80
2 True. Because there is less water in a woman's body and the concentration of alcohol is therefore higher. Also, women tend to weigh less than men.
3 Yes, Yes, No. The only thing that makes you drunk is alcohol, however you take it.
4 BAC 400.
5 BAC 500.
6 False. Your driving gets worse after any amount of alcohol.
7 True.
8 True.
9 True.
10 False. It is people who do not get drunk easily who risk becoming addicted.
11 False. This is nonsense.
12 35.

7

A look forwards and backwards

A look forwards and backwards

This part of the book will help you to look over your progress and give you advice on coping with your drinking in the future

To recap...

Before you read this Part, look over the 'Check Chart' on page 11 to make sure you have completed everything so far.

We have now come to the final part of this self-help guide. In the previous parts you have done the following things:

In Part 2

You identified reasons for cutting down which apply to you and you also discovered that your weekly Grand Total should never exceed 21 units for men and 14 units for women.

In Part 3

You learned something about the way alcohol affects you and, in particular, about Blood Alcohol Concentrations.

In Part 4

You thought over your own reasons for drinking.

In Part 5

You learned and put into practice a range of methods for cutting down your drinking:

1. Keeping a Daily Drinking Diary.
2. Deciding on your personal Drinking Rules.
3. Fixing a Daily Cut-off point for your drinking.

In Part 6

You read about alternatives to drinking in response to particular kinds of problems which may apply to you. If you read all these parts carefully, if you have completed all the exercises we set you, if you have tried to put into practice all the advice we have given you, then you will be well on the way to achieving a lasting reduction in your drinking. **Well done! Congratulations!** We bet you can feel the benefit already. But hang on a moment! You are not out of the woods yet. And you mustn't become too confident about your new drinking habits.

Suppose I have a relapse?

It is quite possible that you are going to have a **relapse**, if indeed you have not done so already. By relapse, we simply mean one or more occasions when you will go over your daily or weekly limits and perhaps break some other Drinking Rules as well.

There are all kinds of reasons for a relapse. It might be the result of some special occasion which interferes with your new drinking behaviour, like going to a wedding or meeting an old friend you used to drink with.

It might also be the result of some extra stress in your life which takes up too much of your emotional energy for you to worry about your drinking any more. There are many other kinds of situations which might bring about a relapse.

The advice given in Parts 5 and 6 about cutting down your drinking can be applied again if your drinking has increased. Just because you have had one relapse, this does not mean that you are back to square one.

Learning is not smooth and unfaltering

You're not out of the woods yet...

One swallow doesn't make a summer

If you are learning to play a sport like golf, your progress will not be a steady improvement week by week. On some days you will do better, but on others you will seem to be doing as badly as you did at the beginning.

Does this mean that you have lost everything you learned on the golf course? Of course not! Learning is not smooth and unfaltering. Exactly the same thing applies to learning to cut down your drinking.

Some days you may do badly and feel as if it is all a waste of time. You might feel as if you are losing control over your habit. 'I'm back to square one', 'It's no use, I can't do it', 'I might as well be hung for a sheep as for a lamb', are perhaps some of the things you might find yourself saying. **These statements are wrong**. Yet the effect of thinking them is to make what you believe to be the case actually come true.

➔ **Think of your relapse as just a slip; it is something you can put behind you and overcome.**

The important thing is not to give up trying to cut down your drinking just because you have had a slip. You must stay calm and you must think carefully about the reasons for it. It is essential that you learn something from the experience. Then, next time the situation which brought about the slip occurs, you will be ready for it and will be able to cope with it without drinking too much.

It is possible to change your daily cut-off point and your drinking rules in the light of experience

One way of leaning from your experience is, of course, to improve the limits and rules you have fixed for your drinking. The weekly Grand Total limit is inflexible–you must not change that–but it is possible to change your Daily Cut-off point and your Drinking Rules in the light of experience.

Obviously we are not suggesting that you should change your rules every other day–that would destroy the point of the whole exercise. But if you find that you keep on going slightly over your cut-off then there might be a case for increasing it, bearing in mind the advice on setting your Daily Cut-off point we gave on page 60.

On the other hand, it might be that your cut-off is too high and needs to be lowered. This might be because your cut-off allows you to become a little 'tipsy' so that you get in the mood for more alcohol and this is hard to resist. If this happens a number of times, then try lowering your cut-off to a point where you don't feel the effects of alcohol in this way.

Give the rules a fair chance to see if they help you cut down

You can also make changes to your other Drinking Rules, like where, when and with whom you drink. Again, don't just change these rules on a whim. Give the rules a fair chance to see if they help you cut down. But, if you find from experience that there is something definitely wrong with one of your rules, then go ahead and improve it.

If you find from experience that there is something definitely wrong with one of your rules, then go ahead and improve it

➔ **Whether or not you have a relapse, there is one time when you should consider changing your personal Drinking Rules. This is after six weeks of filling in your Drinking Diary.**

In Part 4, you decided on your Drinking Rules after looking at four troublesome and four trouble-free drinking sessions. But after keeping your Drinking Diary for six weeks, you will have a lot more information about your drinking which could be used to improve your Drinking Rules, if necessary. So, it will be very useful to do the whole exercise over again. Full details are given in Part 8 on page 103.

Quite apart from sudden relapses, when you may get drunk and break the rules you have set for yourself, there is another danger to be kept in mind. This is the danger of gradually slipping back into your bad old ways, almost without noticing it. We are talking here about a time-scale of months or even years. You may have been able to cut down your drinking now but can you be sure you will be able to keep up the good work in the months and years ahead?

Fortunately, there are things you can do to guard against this danger. As we advised on page 51, you should continue to record your drinking in your 'Pocket Diary' after finishing the Drinking Diary sheets provided on pages 104 to 115.

We suggest that you get into the habit of jotting down your intake every day and that you keep this up for at least a year. After all, it only takes a few seconds of your time.

It is also important to calculate your Grand Total every week to make sure it isn't much trouble and will be well worth it. In the longer term, however, keeping your drinking within safe limits is all about an attitude of mind.

We sincerely hope that, as a result of reading this book, you'll have become much more aware of your own drinking. You are thinking about it more and you understand it much better. What is now needed is for the new awareness to become a permanent part of your experience. It should last you for the rest of your life.

➔ **This change in attitude is the only way of making absolutely sure that you will never drink in a way which does you harm again.**

Suppose I haven't benefited from this book?

If you have reached this far in the book, most of you will have already achieved some success in cutting down your drinking. We are confident that most people who use this book and take it seriously will benefit from it.

There will be other people who have not benefited yet, but who are going to succeed in the near future. This is why you must give the methods described in the book a fair try. Don't give up too quickly. You should persevere with these methods for at **least** the 12 weeks covered by the Drinking Diary in Part 8.

You should persevere for at least twelve weeks

But there may be exceptions. There may be a few people, probably a very few, who will conscientiously use the book for three months or more but who will not succeed in cutting down. There are many reasons why this might happen and there is no point in speculating about it here. It could be that you need specialised help on a face-to-face basis to help you get your drinking under control. It could even be that you are best advised to give up drinking completely.

In either case, you should seek specialised help for your problems from your nearest Council on Alcohol. They will advise you on your best course of action. So, if you do have a drinking problem and, if after giving it a good try, you find that this book hasn't helped you, consult the list of addresses given in Part 8.

8

Drinking diaries and directory

Drinking diaries and directory

Drinking diaries

Before you read this Part, look over the 'Check Chart' on page 11 to make sure you have completed everything so far.

The idea of keeping a Drinking Diary to record your drinking was explained to you in Part 5 (pages 49 to 50). There it was stressed that, to **get the maximum benefit from using this book, you must fill in your Drinking Diary every day**.

Preferably, you should fill it in as soon as possible after drinking while the memory of what you have drunk is still fresh in your mind.

Remember:

1. That you can put both good and bad things down in the 'Consequences of Drinking' column.
2. That you should try out recording each drinking session separately if more than one session in a day.

Finally, remember to complete the Diary for all 12 weeks provided, and to add up the units for each week to make your weekly Grand Total. **This, of course, should always be kept under 21 units for men and 14 units for women**.

Beware of home measures–they often contain more alcohol than a pub-measure

And, in the unlikely event that you have forgotten: one unit equals a half pint of beer, which equals a single whisky, which equals a glass of wine etc. (See the 'Table of Alcohol Strengths' on page 16 to convert different drinks into units of alcohol).

Take care in estimating the number of units in drinks poured at home or at a friend's house, because these often contain more alcohol than a pub-measure.

Liver count 18–09.09.06

Drinking diary week 1

	Day	Time	Hours spent	Place	Who with	Other activities	Cost	Consequences (if any)	Units
Week 1	~~31.08.06~~ Thursday	7.30.	1	home.	Friends on phone	w. T.V.	£1.00	—	2
	01.09.06.	6.30pm	7 1/2	home.	alone + phone	Tel	£5.00	hangover.	14
	02.09.06	9.30pm.	3	pub.	Heigh friend	—	£9.00	none (tired)	4
	3.09.06.	8.30	3	home	friend	computer	£3.00	tired	6
	04.09.06.	7.00.	1	home	T.V	Tel.	£1.00	—	2
~~wk2~~	06.09.06.	9.00.	3	home	Tel.	T.V.	£5.00	h/over.	10
wk 2 →	10.09.06.	6.30.	5	home	tel/work/T.V	"	£8.00	h/over.	12.
	13.09.06.	9.00.	2	home	~~work~~ alone/T.V	work/T.V	£1.00	none	2.
Wk. 3	14.09.06.	~~7.00~~.	5	home	alone	Tel./work	£2.90	tired	11.
	15.09.	7.00pm.	2	at sisters	sister & family	T.V. chatting	£1.20	—	2
	16.09	7.00pm	2	"	"	"	£1.80	—	3
	17.09.	7.00.	4	"	"	"	£2.40	—	4
	18.09.	7.30	2	home	alone	T.V.	90p	—	2
	19.09.	—	—	—	—	—	—	—	—
	20.09.	5.30.		home	~~alone work/Tel~~	work/tel	£4.00	h/over.	8
	21-09	—	—	—	—	—	—	—	—
Week 4	22.09.	7.00.	1	home	alone	T.V. work	£1.00.	—	2
	23.09.	7.30	7	at friends	friends	socialising	£4.00	h/over.	8
	24.09.	—	—	—	—	—	—	—	—
	25.09	6.00.	2	friends	friend	talking			
	~~26.09~~			home	alone	T.V.			
	~~27.0~~								

Grand total for the week: 3

Margin notes: 1 bottle gin + wk 1 Total = 3[illegible]; 14 in Total (ill); 30 units

Drinking diary week 2

Day	Time	Hours spent	Place	Who with	Other activities	Cost	Consequences (if any)	Units
26.09	—	—	—	—	—	—	—	—
27.09.	8.30	4	home Folk club	friends	music	£4.50	h/over	6
28.09.	5.30	1	friends	friends	—	—	—	1
29.09	—	—	—	—	—	—	—	—
30.09	5.30	~~7~~	friends/home	friends		£4.50		~~10~~ 8
1.10.	—	—	—	—	—	—	—	—
2.10.	7.00	5	home	friends on phone	on phone	6.00	tired	12
3.10.	—	—	—	—	—	—	—	—
4.10.	—	—	—	—	—	—	—	—
5.10.								1
06.10	5.00	3.00.	home	sister	cooking cleaning	£2.00	none	4
07.10	7.00.	12.00	home	sister	talking T.V. music	£3.50	tired	6
08.10	—	—	—	—	—	—	—	—
09.10	7.00.	2.	home	alone	work etc.	1.50.	—	2
10.10	5:30	5	at friends home	at home friends	tel work	£4.50		10
11.10	—	—	—	—	—	—	—	—
12.10	6.30.	1.	Relatives home	sister & niece	eating	—	—	1

Grand total for the week ______

wk 5

20 units Total

21

Week 6.

23.

Drinking diary week 3

Week 7

Day	Time	Hours spent	Place	Who with	Other activities	Cost	Consequences (if any)	Units
13.10.06	6.30	8	home	alone + tel.	computer	£7.00	tired + h/over	14
14.10.06	—	—	—	—	—	—	—	—
15.10.06	7.00.	2hrs	home	alone	T.V.	£1.50	none	3
16.10.06	—	—	—	—	—	—	—	—
17.10.06	6.00.	1	home	alone	phone	50p	—	1
18.10.06	6.00.	2.00	friends home	friend + alone	work Tel. T.V	50p	—	3
19.10.06	6.00	1.00.	home	alone friends	work + tel.	£4.00	h/over	13

34

Wk. 8.

Day	Units
20.10.	0
21.10.	10
22.10	0
23.10	1
24.10	1
25.10	0
26.10.	0

12

Wk. 9

Day	Units
27.10.	10
28.10	2
29.10	0
30.10	0
31.10	14
01.11.	0
02.11.	0

26.

Grand total for the week 26

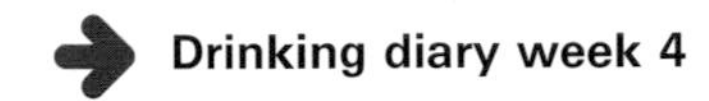

Drinking diary week 4

Day	Time	Hours spent	Place	Who with	Other activities	Cost	Consequences (if any)	Units	
3.11.06.	7.00.	8	home	on tel.	T.V. work	£4	h/over.	14	
4.11.06	5.30	4½	home	friend	comp.	£3	—	3	
5.11.06								—	
6.11.06								—	
7.11.06			home	alone	on Tel			2	
8.11.06			home	alone	T.V. work			1	27
9.11.06			home	alone	tel.	£3	h/ache	7	
10.11.06	8.00	4	friends	friends	socialis	—	—	1	
11.11.06	6.00.	1.00	~~friends~~ at home	friends	social	£3.00	h/over	10	
12.11.06	—	—	—	—			—	0	
13.11		—	—	—	—		—	0	
14.11	6.00.	7	home	alone	Tel.	4.00.	H/over.	10	
15.11								0	23
16.11	6.00	2	friends	friends	soc	—	—	2	
17.11	6.30.	~~1.00~~ 7	home	alone	tel.	£6	h/over	12	
18.11	6.30.	7	~~home~~ friends	friends	soc	£6	h/over.	10	
19.11								0	34
20.11								0	
21.11	6.00	100	at friends	a home	T.V	£3.00	tired	12	
22.11	—	—						0	
23.11							Grand total for the week	0	

Drinking diary week 5

Day	Time	Hours spent	Place	Who with	Other activities	Cost	Consequences (if any)	Units	
24.11	6.00	5	home	alone	tel. park.		tired	6	
25.11	7.00	8.1	home	"	tel.		–	2	
26.11	7.00	5	home	"	tel		h/over.	12	
27.11								0	
28.11							h/over.	8	28
29.11								0	
30.11								0	
1.12.								6	
2.12								3	
3.12								0	
4.12								0	
5.12								2	
6.12.								8	25
7.12								8	
8.12							h/over	0	
9.12							h/over.	12	
10.12								0	
11.12								0	27
13.12								1	
14.12								14	
15.12								0	
							Grand total for the week	27	

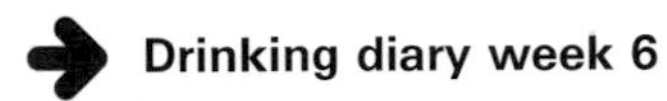

Drinking diary week 6

Day	Time	Hours spent	Place	Who with	Other activities	Cost	Consequences (if any)	Units
10.01.07								
11								
12								
13								
14								
15								
16								
						Grand total for the week		

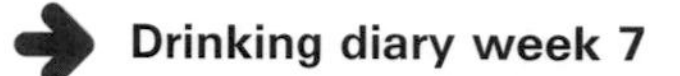

Drinking diary week 7

Day	Time	Hours spent	Place	Who with	Other activities	Cost	Consequences (if any)	Units
							Grand total for the week	

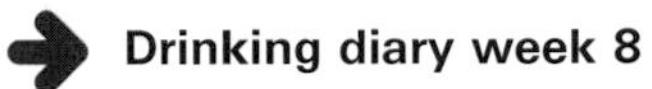

Drinking diary week 8

Day	Time	Hours spent	Place	Who with	Other activities	Cost	Consequences (if any)	Units

Grand total for the week ______

Drinking diary week 9

Day	Time	Hours spent	Place	Who with	Other activities	Cost	Consequences (if any)	Units
							Grand total for the week	

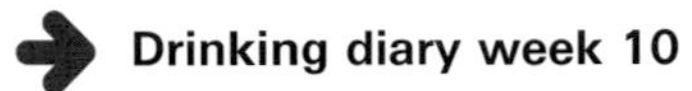

Drinking diary week 10

Day	Time	Hours spent	Place	Who with	Other activities	Cost	Consequences (if any)	Units
							Grand total for the week	

Drinking diary week 11

Day	Time	Hours spent	Place	Who with	Other activities	Cost	Consequences (if any)	Units

Grand total for the week ______

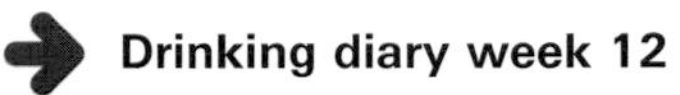

Drinking diary week 12

Day	Time	Hours spent	Place	Who with	Other activities	Cost	Consequences (if any)	Units
							Grand total for the week	

Revised drinking rules

After six weeks of keeping your Drinking Diary you will have a lot of information on the way you drink. You should, therefore, repeat the exercise first set on pages 52-55–the exercise aimed at making a set of personal Drinking Rules.

Look over your Drinking Diary and find the last four occasions when drinking caused you trouble–in other words, occasions when you went over your Daily Cut-off point or broke some other rule. When you have done this, copy down the information on to page 117. (Don't worry if you can't find four troublesome drinking occasions: put down as many as you have. If you can't find any, there is no need to do this exercise).

Now find four occasions when you drank without any trouble and kept within your limit. Now see whether there is anything common to the first four occasions and anything common to the second four. Write down these common features on page 118. Write as many as you can find. You are now in a position to change your Drinking Rules, if necessary. See page 55 for a full explanation of how to arrive at your Drinking Rules and then write any changed rules below.

My revised drinking rules

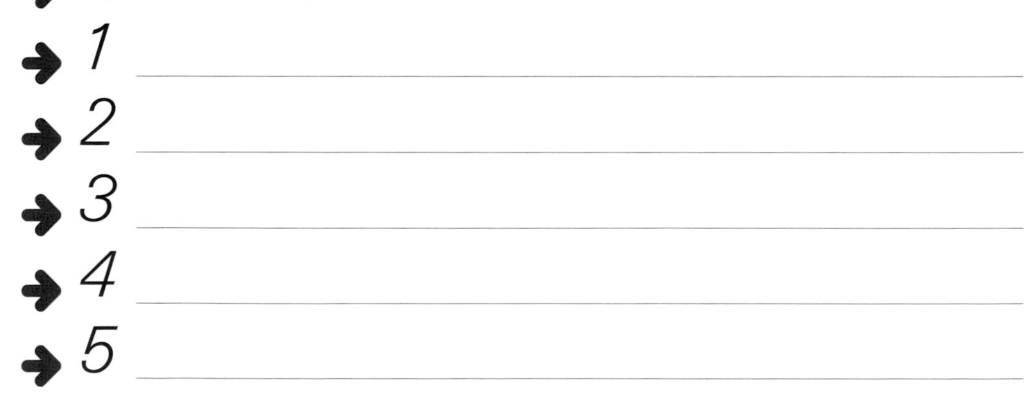

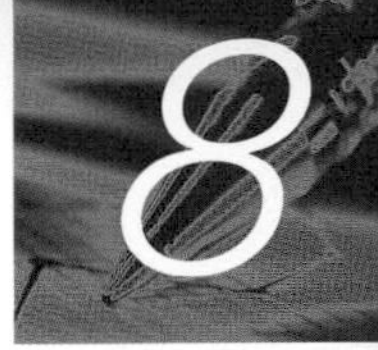

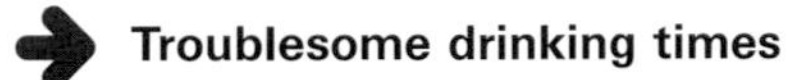

Troublesome drinking times

	Day	Time spent	Hours	Place	Who with	Other activities	Cost	Consequences (if any)	Units
Time *1*									
Time *2*									
Time *3*									
Time *4*									

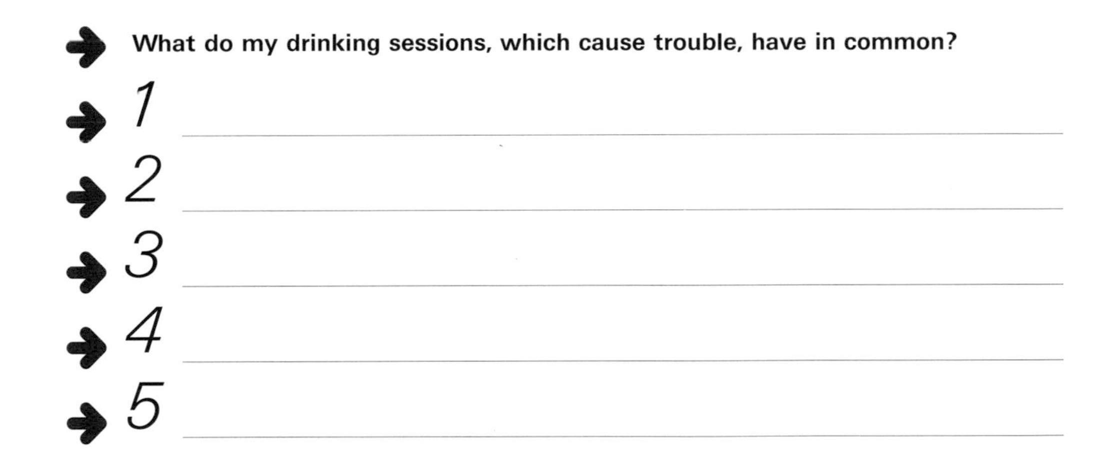

What do my drinking sessions, which cause trouble, have in common?

1 ______________________

2 ______________________

3 ______________________

4 ______________________

5 ______________________

Trouble-free drinking times

	Day	Time spent	Hours	Place	Who with	Other activities	Cost	Consequences (if any)	Units
Time 1									
Time 2									
Time 3									
Time 4									

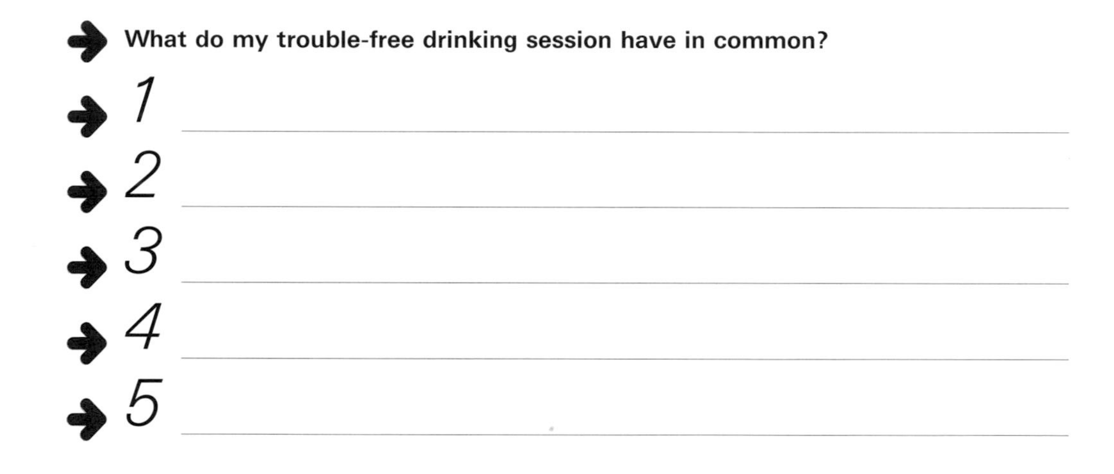

What do my trouble-free drinking session have in common?

1. ____________________
2. ____________________
3. ____________________
4. ____________________
5. ____________________

Drinking graph

As explained in Part 5, a very good way of rewarding your success in cutting down drinking is to be able to see at a glance the progress you have made on a graph.

This will also be useful as a warning if you start to slide back into your bad drinking habits. Keeping a Drinking Graph is absolutely simple. All you have to do is note how much you have drunk each week–the weekly Grand Total from your Drinking Diaries on pages 104 to 115–and then put a small cross on the appropriate column in the Graph. We have already drawn on the graph the safe limits for men (21 units) and for women (14 units).

Here's what you have to do to keep the graph:

1. Note your weekly Grand Total for Week 1 in your Drinking Diary on page 104. Look at the column on the Graph with '1' under it at the bottom of the page. Run a finger up the column until you come to the number which corresponds to your weekly Grand Total. Then put a small cross at this point.
2. After you have done this, write in the date of the last day of Week 1 under the figure '1' at the bottom of the page.
3. After the second week of keeping your Drinking Diary, do the same thing for Week 2. Put a cross at the correct place on the column with '2' underneath it and then fill in the date below.
4. When you have done that, join up the two crosses for Weeks 1 and 2 by drawing a straight line between them.
5. Put a cross on the graph for every week of your Drinking Diary and join up the crosses as you go along.
6. Now sit back and admire the way the line charting your drinking is going steadily down or, at least, keeping to a safe and healthy level.
7. If the line starts going up again and especially if it goes over the safe limit, ask yourself what has happened to your drinking and then do something about it. Go back and read Parts 5 and 6 again.

8

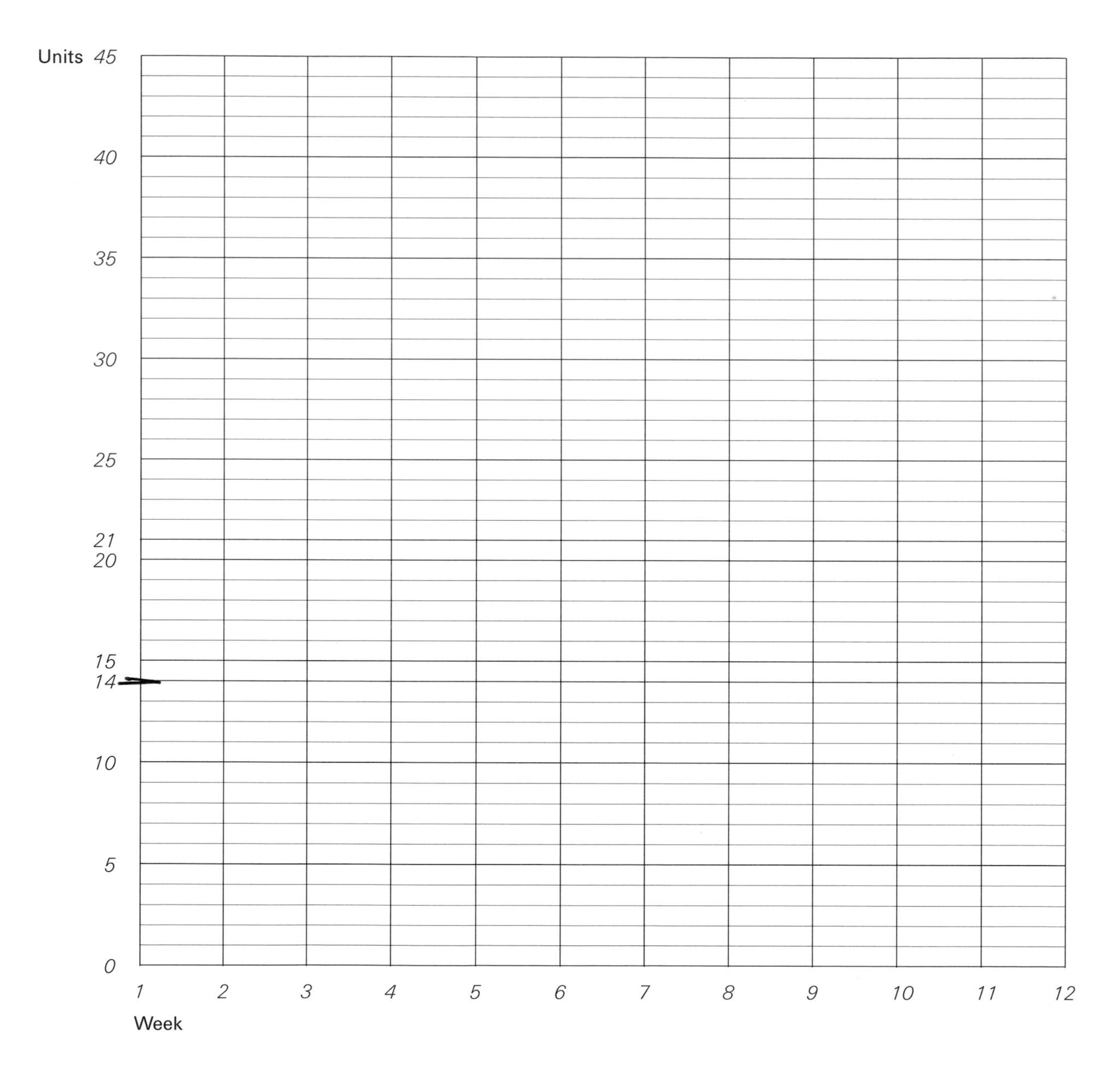
Units
45
40
35
30
25
21
20
15
14
10
5
0
1
2
3
4
5
6
7
8
9
10
11
12
Week

Directory

 Further information can be obtained from your doctor, nurse or from your local alcohol advice centre.

 Drinkline is the UK national helpline which provides confidential information and advice about alcohol.
Telephone: 0800 917 8282
Hours: Monday – Friday 9am – 11pm
Saturday 6pm – 11pm Sunday 6pm – 11pm

 In Scotland, Alcohol Focus Scotland is the central coordinating body for a large number of local councils on alcohol. The services they offer vary, but they will be able to put you in touch with the best help available in your area. Contact:

Alcohol Focus Scotland
166 Buchanan Street
Glasgow G1 2LW
Telephone: 0141 572 6700

The pocket diary

➜ **You've read the book–now keep the diary!**

➜ Now that you have finished reading the book, we advise you to keep it in a safe place so that you can come back to it if you need to. After you have completed the diary pages in the book, you should continue to keep track of your drinking in the pocket diary. The diary also contains the list of methods for cutting down your drinking. This will be a useful reminder to carry with you.

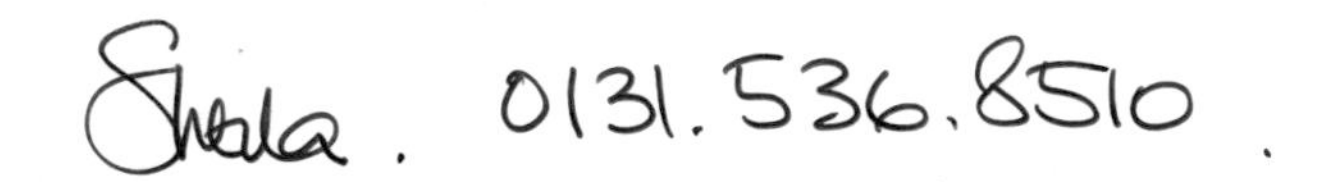